Math Activities for Child Involvement

ENOCH DUMAS

University of California, Berkeley

ALLYN and BACON, Inc.   BOSTON

Library of Congress Catalog Card No. 79-155310

Printed in the United States of America.

Fourth printing . . . March, 1973

CONTENTS

PREFACE

In this book can be found hundreds of suggested projects, manipulative materials, games, puzzles, riddles, and other resource items which can spark children's learning. This is not intended to be a book of explanations of mathematics or of methods of teaching it, but a book of ideas to draw from as you involve children in their own learning.

Children do best what they like to do. What they like to do may be hard work, but that, too, may be part of the fun—to be stimulated, excited, surprised, spurred to competition, amused by ridiculous rewards for success. The purpose of this book is to suggest a variety of activities that will bring that kind of mental and emotional involvement into the learning of mathematics.

No attempt is made to be exhaustive with regard to either the extent or the variety of possibilities. Creative teachers may find many ways of modifying or adding to what is presented in this book. But if the ideas suggested on the pages that follow can assist teachers or parents in helping children gain appreciation for and develop competence in elementary mathematics, then the purpose of the author will have been achieved.

ACKNOWLEDGMENTS

The author is indebted to the many students, teachers, and others who, wittingly or unwittingly, contributed ideas which could be adapted for *Math Activities*. He hopes the finished product will justify their contributions and will help teachers and parents make arithmetic the pleasant study it deserves to be.

Among the many entries listed in this book, readers will find adaptations of some old favorites which have appeared in various publications over a span of many years. With whom they originated, the writer does not know and, therefore, is unable to give credit.

Special appreciation should go to the late Jens Lloyd Lund who, before his untimely death, critically read the first draft of the manuscript for *Math Activities* and made many helpful suggestions. The author acknowledges with appreciation the insightful reviews of the manuscript by Professor C. W. Schminke, University of Oregon and Professor Rob Moore, San Francisco State College. Among the many others who gave generous assistance are Nancy Blau, Joan Cheifetz, Dorothy and Richard Demorest, Graham Rankin, Sue Shaffer, Ronald Traill, my daughter, Judy, and my wife, Margaret. The writer assumes responsibility for any mistakes or shortcomings and welcomes corrections or suggestions by readers.

Chapter 1

MATH ACTIVITIES AND YOU

Mathematics has become an increasingly fascinating and important study in recent years. Many children are excited by the orderliness of mathematics, by the sheer fun of manipulating numbers, by the scientific achievements possible through the use of mathematics, by the discovery of a surprise relationship, or by the solution of a puzzling problem.

The negative attitudes that children and adults may hold about mathematics are learned. Usually they can be traced to prior pressure to learn something that was either incomprehensible or boring or both. When children are frustrated or bored, changes need to be made.

From the beginning, mathematics should be made understandable to the learner. With the materials and activities described in this and other books, ways can be found whereby all children can understand the concepts and principles suitable to their levels of development.[1] Much of the mystifying element can be taken out of mathematics, and children can learn to appreciate the logic and order on which mathematical facts and computational procedures are based.

All learning in mathematics should be enjoyable. Emphasize the pleasure and interest, not the amount to be covered. Believe

---

[1] One such book is J. Marks, C. Purdy, and L. Kinney, *Teaching Elementary Mathematics for Understanding* (New York: McGraw-Hill Book Company, 1970.)

in this and then act upon it. If children enjoy their work, they will learn a great deal. And, more importantly, they will develop an abiding interest in mathematics.

The learning of combinations (basic facts) and procedures should and can be made interesting. Such learning is essential to efficient calculation, but for many children it is the most boring part of mathematics. This can be changed. From the pages that follow, select interesting and challenging puzzles, bulletin boards, games, and manipulative materials, such as numbers 3–6, 3–27, 4–3, and 4–46. Place them on tables or shelves to make them available to children or include them in directed activity. Above all, let your own enthusiasm and interest show.

Children learn if they are expected to learn. Over the years a great deal of evidence,[2] both formal and informal, has accumulated to support the thesis that when parents and teachers expect high levels of performance from children, the tendency is for them to fulfill those expectations. And the opposite seems to be true also—when little is expected, little is likely to be achieved. A mother says, "Sammy's father was no good at math and neither was I. Sammy isn't going to be any different." Such talk is not likely to encourage the boy. Nor is this by a teacher talking to a visitor, "This is my slow group so I just give them easy assignments."

Of course one may set expectations too high and so discourage the learner, particularly if he has little confidence in his own abilities.[3] Comparing a child of moderate ability with one who made unusual achievement may have serious negative effects. Avoid such comments as, "Why can't you be like your brother? He was a whiz at math."

The following is a list of some practical teaching suggestions:

1. Gear tasks to children's development levels.[4] For example,

---

[2] *See* R. Rosenthal and L. Jacobson, *Pygmalion in the Classroom* (New York: Holt, Rinehart and Winston, Inc., 1968).

[3] *See* W. D. LaBenne and B. I. Greene, *Educational Implications of Self-Concept Theory* (Pacific Palisades, California: Goodyear Publishing Company, Inc., 1969), especially Chapter 10.

[4] Brief accounts of child development levels relevant to learning mathematics may be found in such books as C. H. Howard and Enoch Dumas, *Basic Procedures in Teaching Arithmetic* (Boston: D. C. Heath and Company, 1963), pp. 17–33 and 134–140, and Klaas Kramer, *The Teaching of Elementary School Mathematics* (Boston: Allyn and Bacon, Incorporated, 1966), pp. 115–132.

kindergarteners learning to count may profit by an activity such as that described in number 2–1, while sixth graders who have reached a stage of abstract thinking may be encouraged to select for investigation from the list in number 7–9.

2. Proceed from concrete to abstract experiences. Most elementary school children learn mathematics first by manipulating real things, such as learning the meaning of 3 + 2 by joining a set of three buttons and a set of two buttons to make a set of five buttons. A next step may involve representations of real things (semi-concrete—pictures of things, dots, short line segments, geometric figures, "tickets" in a pocket chart, etc.), such as drawing a mark around a set of three dots and a set of two dots to show a set of five dots. More abstract would be filling the square in $3 + 2 = \square$ with the numeral for five. In this book will be found items illustrative of each step, e.g., concrete—number 2–4, semi-concrete— number 4–24, and abstract—number 4–46. If children have difficulty understanding an abstract number problem, help them grasp it by illustrating with semi-concrete or concrete representations.

3. Be sure that understanding precedes practice for mastery. A place value chart (see number 2–89) may be used to illustrate borrowing in subtraction, but only when the concept is understood should the child practice subtraction computations involving borrowing.

4. Encourage children to discover concepts or facts. Sometimes discovery comes through exploration as when a child manipulates Cuisenaire rods (see number 2–8) and discovers that all those of a given color are the same length. At other times a problem is posed and questions raised, often by the teacher, until pupils find a solution; Pascal's triangle (number 3–100) lends itself to such a procedure.

5. Alternate active with passive things to do. Children should not be kept sitting for long periods of time with no opportunity to move about; the younger the pupils, the shorter should be the sedentary periods. If children have been doing "seatwork" at their desks, play a game such as "Going to the City," number 3–44.

6. Help children to feel secure with their classmates and their teacher. This important principle is reflected in the suggestions for the use of games, page 15.

7. Make it possible for *all* children to experience success. Note, for example, the suggestions for using puzzles on page 16.

8. Loosen the reins on children by giving them some choice of activities and materials. A teacher not confident of class control can limit choices of activities, but do provide choice.

THE ORGANIZATION OF THE BOOK

Readers will note that the contents of this book are organized around major topics in elementary school mathematics. Many activities can be adapted for use with more than one topic. Cross references indicate many of these adaptable items.

Items are identified by chapter number followed by the item number within the chapter, e.g., 2–9 indicates chapter 2, item 9.

The mathematics activities described in succeeding chapters are given under the following headings: Activities and Projects, Instructional Materials, History, Games, Puzzles, Shortcuts, Tricks, Verses, and Music. While not every kind of activity or material appears under each mathematics topic, the foregoing order is generally maintained to assist the reader to locate quickly what he is looking for.

Where feasible, items most suitable for young children appear first in a given list. Answers are provided to save time for teachers and parents. Children should have access to them only when checking solutions.

SUGGESTIONS FOR USING THE MATERIALS IN THE BOOK

While readers may have perfectly acceptable ways of using the material contained in this book, the suggestions which follow indicate the classroom uses envisioned by the author. Parents will need to adapt recommendations to suit their needs.

Activities and projects

A Chinese proverb reads

I hear, and I forget;
I see, and I remember;
I do, and I understand.

Children should be involved in the planning and execution of projects which require the *use* of mathematical skills and understandings. Not only are children more likely to remember mathematical concepts which are used in "real life" situations, but also they are likely to develop a greater appreciation and understanding of the important role of mathematics in our culture.

An example is given below of how a study of trains could lend itself to a non-textbook approach to the teaching of mathematics. The suggested activities would need to be adapted to the ability levels of the children involved.

1. Preparation for a study trip to the train yards.
   a. Estimating the distance to and from the railroad yards.
   b. Estimating the time needed for the excursion.
   c. Calculating the cost per person.
   d. Determining the number of cars needed.
   e. Recording the money as received.

2. At the train yards—collecting information needed to carry on such follow-up activities as construction, dramatic play, problem solving (illustrated), and making graphs and tables.
   a. Sketching the general layout of the railway yard.
   b. Measuring the width of tracks and the sizes of various kinds of railway cars, locomotives, and other equipment.
   c. Finding out capacities and total weights of various kinds of railway cars.
   d. Recording weight, size, power, and use of various kinds of locomotives.
   e. Learning how and why cars and locomotives are numbered.
   f. Learning about signals, mile posts, and safety devices.
   g. Sketching speed boards and learning about the data recorded.
   h. Collecting dining car menus.
   i. Counting tables and chairs in the dining car.
   j. Collecting time tables and asking about standard time and daylight saving time.
   k. Getting information about tickets to various places, round trip fares, purpose and disposition of tickets.
   l. Discovering how freight is weighed.
   m. Seeing how bills of lading and waybills are filled out.
   n. Getting information on freight rates for different kinds of merchandise.
   o. Noting how various kinds of freight are loaded and the space requirements.
   p. Learning about train speeds and speed limits.
   q. Gathering information about refrigerator cars and temperatures for meat, fruit, and other perishables.

   r. Finding out what kinds of fuel are used, how stored, and amounts consumed.

   s. Learning about wages earned by employees according to jobs.

   t. Getting information on the many kinds of costs involved in running a railroad.

3. Problems to solve in the classroom by discussion, research, asking others, using pencil and paper, or a combination of these.

   a. Calculating freight rates for different weights of cargo to go different distances.

   b. Calculating the cost of a trip on a train if the charge is five cents per mile and the distance traveled is 280 miles, 340 miles, etc.

   c. Comparing the average wages of railway workers with others.

   d. Computing the number of freight cars required for given amounts of cattle, sheep, automobiles, coal, wheat, lumber, or other commodities.

   e. Calculating the approximate time required for a trip when given the average speed and the distance.

   f. Calculating the approximate distance traveled when given the average speed and the time required for the trip.

   g. Calculating the average speed when given the distance and the time required for the trip.

   h. Comparing the size, weight, and horsepower of various types of engines.

   i. Making a time line of important dates in the history of railways.

   j. Comparing the speed limits for various kinds of trains.

   k. Making a chart of the required temperatures for refrigerator cars carrying different types of produce, as bananas, peaches, lettuce, grapefruit, etc.

   l. Computing how much fuel is required to carry an average freight train between two selected major cities.

   m. Comparing the lengths of railway lines between selected cities and the "bee line" distance.

To provide children with other real problems requiring the use of mathematical skills and concepts, involve them in the planning and execution of many kinds of projects.

Too often parents and teachers do all the "real life" mathematical problems and leave the artificial ones to children, e.g., the adult does all the counting, measuring, and calculating incidental to a party, but children must work from textbooks and workbooks. Parents should involve their children in discussions and activities related to home repairs (How large a board is needed to replace a broken shelf? How much paint is required to cover bedroom walls and is it more advantageous to buy by the quart or the gallon? Should we rebuild the broken backyard gate ourselves or hire a carpenter?); gardening (How long should a row of carrots be to supply an adequate amount? Seeds should be planted how far apart, how deeply? How many rows can we get from the size of plot available?); family money management (How much can we afford for a family vacation and how much money must we set aside each month? How much will school clothes cost to start the new term? How much does it cost us to leave lights burning unnecessarily?); and the like. Teachers should include children in much of the classroom planning and ordering of books and supplies (How many books can we buy for the $100 we are allotted? How many pencils and erasers will pupils need this term? What and how much colored construction paper will we need for special events this year?); making murals (How much space will we need? How much space can be provided for each committee? How large should close-up figures be made?); preparing for a play day (What markings will be needed on the play yard for each event? How much space should be set aside for volley ball? How can we make good circles for the marble tournament?); and the like.

Suggested projects to involve and interest children will be found throughout the book under the heading of "Activities."

Instructional materials

A characteristic of modern methods of teaching mathematics is the use of a wide assortment of teaching materials. Other things being equal, the greater the use of well selected aids, the greater will be children's understanding of abstract ideas and the greater will be their motivation to learn.

There are no magical items without which the arithmetic program cannot succeed. When the budget is a problem, homemade materials and articles collected in the community can serve the teacher or parent very well. Some things can be made by children. Of course some materials available only commercially might add considerably to learning situations and also may save much teacher or parent time.

Descriptions of instructional materials are presented throughout the book under topic headings to which they are appropriate. A few general suggestions follow.

1. In general, teaching materials, like toys, are best if their uses are multiple, e.g., blocks of varying sizes, shapes, surfaces, and colors lend themselves to more creative activity and make discoveries more likely than do blocks that are all alike.

2. Materials should appeal to as many senses as possible. Consider how items can be made interesting to touch as well as to look at. The senses of hearing and of smelling may be more difficult to provide for, though for hearing, consider using tape recorders, which are now becoming popular both at home and at school.

3. Teachers report that children often are pleased when told that certain "home-made" materials were constructed especially for them.

4. Keep in mind the safety of children by avoiding sharp corners, slivers, harmful paints, and the like.

5. Except when the nature of an activity requires it, avoid marbles and similiar things that roll off desks and tables. When beans are suggested for games and other activities, select large, flat kinds.

6. With very young children, construct or gather materials large enough for easy handling and too large to poke into noses or ears.

7. Cards which need to be in packs "right side up" can be quickly arranged for use if the corner of each card is cut or notched. A common playing card size is 2¼" x 3½". Paper stock used in making cards is generally 60 to 70 pound Bristol board, glossy finish.

8. Here are some suggestions for chart making.[5]
   a. Make all charts of the same size and material. Oak tagboard, 24" x 18", is very good.
   b. Mark lines ¾" apart and use a brush pen—¼" for primary grades and ⅛" for upper grades.
   c. Mount pictures with rubber cement. Include some color on each chart.

---

[5] For examples of arithmetic charts, *see* Enoch Dumas, Charles F. Howard, and Jean E. Dumas, *Arithmetic Charts Handbook* (Palo Alto, Calif.: Fearon Publishers, 1960), and *Charts for the New Math* (Palo Alto, Calif.: Fearon Publishers, 1966).

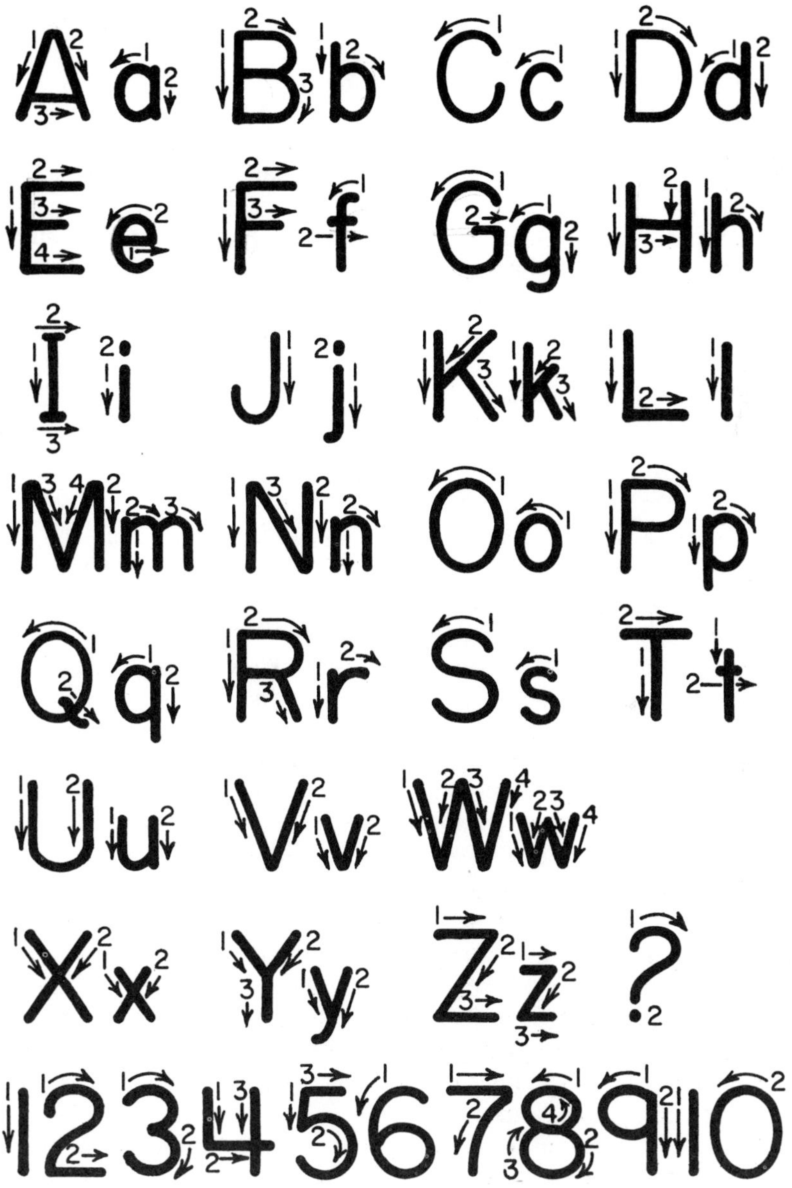

    d. Follow manuscript forms used in school—especially at primary grade levels. (See figure below.) Observe approved punctuating, capitalizing, spelling, and grammar.

    e. Store charts by rolling loosely and tying with a string or place flat in a large box or drawer.

9. Most instructional materials should be available to children whenever they are interested and have time. Plan to locate items at various places around the room or home. Some teachers provide a "math center." However the materials are displayed, time should be set aside for children to use materials in exploring mathematics. Such independent study may need to be guided initially.

10. Bulletin boards should be designed to encourage children to ask questions or to carry out appropriate activities; it is not enough that they be attractive.

History

The study of the history of mathematics can help children in several ways, as follows:

1. Develop an appreciation of the contributions of mathematicians and others down through the ages. Note that many kinds of persons made discoveries or invented procedures which led to further development and application. There were those who found mathematics a source of pleasure as was probably the case with the unknown ancient inventor of the magic square; those who combined mathematics and philosophy as did Napier, Leibniz and Descartes; those who found mathematics necessary to scientific study, as did Newton; and so on.

Then there is the appreciation of what has been and can be done through the use of mathematics, from the construction of the Egyptian pyramids to supersonic jet passenger planes, from crude measurements of the circumference of the earth to highly precise measurements of the distance to great stars so far away they can be seen only through the most powerful telescopes, from the navigation of sailing ships to space travel. The list can be extended almost indefinitely.

2. Understand numeration systems and computation procedures by learning how these changed through the centuries from those that were cumbersome and primitive to those which can be programmed for electronic computers. A study such as that of a simple, hand-operated adding machine can provide insight with regard to our decimal numeration system. Who can learn how to perform lattice multiplying without increasing his knowledge of the basic procedures of multiplication?

3. Understand the relationship of mathematics to other curricular areas. For example, the industrial revolution could not have taken place without the application of a rapidly improving system of mathematics; the Mayans could not have produced their sophisticated calendar without a means to calculate positions and movements of heavenly bodies; the high level of our standard of living could not have been achieved without the electrical engineering made possible through the discovery of the complex numbers and operations on them. In the foregoing, note how social studies, science, and mathematics are combined. Consider how histories of civilizations are affected by the sophistication of their mathematics. Health, comfort, travel, wealth, taxes, and other attributes of civilization depend on mathematics.

A study of the development of mathematical terms as suggested in number 2–103 demonstrates one way in which language arts and mathematics may be integrated.

Art and music have their dependence on mathematics as is well depicted in the excellent film, *Donald in Mathemagic Land.*[6] The ancient Greeks used the golden rectangle[7] (in which the width is to the length as the length is to the sum of the length and the width) in art and architecture, and it continues in use today, such as in the design of the United Nations' building. Our familiar music scale is based on the mathematics of vibrating strings, e.g., the vibrations per second or the pitch of a given tone is double that of the same tone an octave lower.

Many forms of gambling and amusement are mathematically based and form a study known as game theory. A simple example is shown by tabulating the chances of a flipped coin coming up heads, or the ancient game of guessing whether the number of small objects held in a closed hand is odd or even. Children might investigate and discuss the relation of chance to skill in amusements from checkers to slot machines. Activities of this

---

[6] *Donald in Mathemagic Land,* Walt Disney Productions, 800 Sonora Avenue, Glendale, California, 91201.

[7] The ratio of the golden rectangle (sometimes called the golden section) is about 61.8 to 100 or, for children's drawings, 3 to 5.

kind are appropriate especially to those parts of social studies units dealing with recreation or with family economics.

When superstitions are studied in a social studies program, call attention to beliefs about magical properties of numbers. Perhaps pupils may be led to investigate the belief that bad luck accompanies the number 13, or why 7 appears frequently in ancient literature.

In the curricular area devoted to literature, one may include biographies of mathematicians. For references consult library card catalogs or encyclopedias. Educationally advanced children, as well as older slow learners, may be encouraged to search for information about mathematicians and then write biographies for classmates or for deposit in the school library.

4. Develop versatility in problem solving, which is one of the objectives of the teaching of contemporary mathematics in the elementary school. Versatility is increased when one knows more than one way to get correct answers. The study of historical procedures for solving problems or for performing computations points out a variety of approaches.

5. Provide pleasure through studies into the history of man's colorful advance from a simple primitive life to a highly complex one we call modern civilization. History abounds with interesting problems and ingenious solutions, with blind groping for elusive ideas which now seem very simple, with strange ways of recording numbers, with remarkable engineering feats despite cumbersome mathematical tools. This vast wonderland holds almost endless possibilities for intrinsic motivation, but first "the pump must be primed." The enthusiasm of the teacher or parent and his creative approaches to encourage independent or group study are keys to exciting the children's own interest.

6. Project themselves into the future through an appreciation of the increasing momentum of discovery and application in every phase of mathematics. Someone has commented that those who do not know history will be forever bound by it, implying that those who know the way discoveries have been made and the benefits that have been achieved through applications of knowledge can avoid the mistakes of the past and profit by the successes.

Speculations about the future of mathematics and of its uses are activities that may be used to challenge most boys and girls. Perhaps some can pretend that they have taken a trip into space and returned to earth 50 years from now. What will they find? The more they have learned about the past and the present, the more intelligent their guesses are likely to be.

Games

Games and a game-like atmosphere during the mathematics period help create and sustain interest. They are particularly useful to prevent drill and practice from becoming dull. Few games described in this book fit initial teaching situations, but the teacher can and should provide an atmosphere of delight and fun as children explore and discover mathematical relationships.

Select games in the light of children's needs. If in analyzing practice papers or diagnostic tests, a child or several children are found to make errors in certain combinations, such as 7×8 or 6×9, or in given procedures, such as borrowing from the hundreds' place in the subtraction algorism, choose such games as number 3–66 or number 3–108.

Finding a winner is not always necessary; pupils may enjoy an activity for its own sake.

When a game requires teams, let children name them in some interest-getting manner, e.g., use the names of local or nationally prominent teams or invent names like Scintillating Cipherers, Illustrious Elucidators, Vigorous Logicians, or Associated Digit Counters. Give a winner a fancy title such as Champion of Mathematasia or pin on him a medal of honor "straight from the King of Numeratus."

Be sure all children know how to play a game before actual play starts. Explain, demonstrate, answer questions, go through a short trial, raise questions with those children least likely to understand, and do whatever else seems necessary. Stop a game and explain again if it becomes obvious that someone is off the track.

Sometimes keeping score is necessary or desired. This may be done occasionally by the teacher and at other times by a selected pupil or teacher's aide. Whenever possible, teach children to keep scores. The scorekeeper may be designated also as the umpire or referee.

Fix time limits for games and, if possible, give a warning signal a few minutes before the end of the period.

Some games can be kept accessible to children who have completed other work. Provide game space in areas least likely to distract other pupils.

When playing relay games, avoid having teams so large that children have long waits with nothing to do.

Puzzles

In addition to reinforcing general interest in problem-solving, boys and girls may develop versatile ability to tackle problems through puzzle-solving activity. Children learn that finding solutions often requires shifting from one approach to another; the mind-set established by the way a question is presented, or through one part solved in a particular way, may interfere with further solution unless the worker "plays it loose;" for example, having correctly filled the blank in 4, 8, 16, 32, ____, he may have difficulty with 61, 52, 63, 94, 46, ____. (Reverse the digits in each numeral. One then has 16, 25, 36, 49, 64, ____.) Teachers and parents need to give children experiences that will develop flexibility in their thinking about mathematics.

Puzzles should not be forced on children but be made available to those who are interested.

While solving a puzzle supplies an intrinsic reward, some children may need more. Special praise, a "hero's badge" or a name written on the chalkboard in colored chalk, may help sustain interest for some children. But frequent recognition of the boys and girls who succeed often may have a negative effect on those who rarely solve a puzzle or win a game. If extrinsic rewards are used, it may be better that they be given to a group or a team than to individuals.

Let children solve what puzzles they can and want to but do not give answers. Also encourage children not to share answers among themselves; form a Puzzlers' Association, the members of which, like those of the magicians' union, never tell "how it was done."

Shortcuts

Once boys and girls have developed facility in computations, they are ready to increase speed. In part, this may come from practice on basic algorisms but as insights develop, shortcuts may be uncovered.

Use the discovery approach to help children see that the variations in procedure found in shortcuts follow accepted mathematical principles. For example, in number 4–49, note that $3 \times 3 \times 3$ is another name for 27 and, hence, multiplying three times successively by 3 must accomplish the same end as multiplying by 27; in fact, multiplying by any other substitute for 27 will do the same thing, e.g., $(20 + 7) \times 342 = (20 \times 342) + (7 \times 342)$ —here the distributive principle must be applied.

Sometimes, as in the double column addition procedure described on page 172, the shortcut is more likely to produce errors than the longer process it supplants. Estimating what would be a reasonable answer or some other means of checking should be encouraged.

Let children learn those shortcuts that interest them. Trying to learn a great many may lead to confusion and inaccuracies. Computation contests often stimulate boys and girls to master shortcut procedures.

Some readers may consider the "shortcut" more cumbersome than the process it replaces. Until facility in the new process is achieved, this may very well be true. For the time being, then, the "shortcut" may assume the identity of a trick or oddity.

Oddities and patterns

As people have manipulated numbers in millions of different ways, many startling results have been noted. Some that may be of interest to elementary school pupils are described in pages that follow though not separately listed as oddities or patterns. Some items have characteristics which could be described appropriately under any or all of several designations, as tricks, or oddities, or patterns. Examples of such items are 3–92, 3–93, 3–100, and 3–106. The way each is viewed by the reader may cause him to differ with the writer's classification.

Children should be encouraged to look for reasons why the strange findings occur, e.g., why is the sum made up of ones' digits when a person adds $\begin{smallmatrix} 123456789 \\ 987654321 \\ + \quad\quad 1 \end{smallmatrix}$? A bit of study will reveal that in each place the sum is ten (except the first where one is added to make the final sum pattern consistent) plus the carry

number which is always one making a total of 11; so at each
place, one is recorded and ten is carried. Pupils might experiment
to see if similar findings emerge when selected pairs of numbers
(plus one) are added, as $\begin{array}{r} 246 \\ 864 \\ + 1 \\ \hline \end{array}$ or if the order is changed, as $\begin{array}{r} 927 \\ 183 \\ + 1 \\ \hline \end{array}$.

Many teachers have a "discovery period" where children are
allowed to explore mathematics on their own and record their
findings, odd or otherwise, for a sharing period. Perhaps these
can be collected and displayed on the bulletin board, reported in
the class newspaper, or listed in the class yearbook.

Tricks

For most people, the major value attached to facility in arithmetic is its usefulness as a tool for the solution of quantitative
problems. But at times the tool may be merely a source of pleasure
just as an automobile serves both as a means for getting from one
place to another and to give enjoyment when one goes for a ride.

Children may find pleasure in examining and "trying out" some
of the mathematics tricks described under appropriate headings
in the chapters that follow. Some of the tricks provide them with
insight regarding some of the principles and procedures of number
operations and relationships. Practice in fundamental operations
may be a bonus.

Tricks described in this book provide another resource for the
teacher or parent who wants to help a child have fun with mathematics.

Verses

The verses and rhymes found in this book are presented mainly
because their reading or reciting is fun and not because the writer
thinks much arithmetic is learned or practiced through such
activities. For instance, learning to name the numerals one, two,
three, four in the proper sequence probably is easier than to
memorize

> "One for the money,
> Two for the show,

> Three to make ready,
> And four to go."

On the other hand, some verses serve as helpful memory aids, as, "Thirty days hath September, . . . ," number 7–30.

Music

Teachers and parents skilled in music may find many ways of associating mathematics with it and so make the pursuit of both more interesting. For example: (1) Children may find some similarities between an octave in music and mod seven[8] if they associate do, re, mi, fa, sol, la, ti, do with 0, 1, 2, 3, 4, 5, 6, 0; proceeding seven notes up or down the scale from a given note gets one to the same note again. (2) Fractional notes follow the mathematics of rational numbers, e.g., four quarter notes are equivalent to a whole note. (3) Similarly, ¾ time means that there are three beats to a measure and each quarter note gets one beat; then, two eighth notes will get one beat or one half note will get two beats. Music activities are described in items numbered 2–84 and 7–38.

The correlation of mathematics with other curricular areas may help boys and girls see how mathematics serves as a tool for many vocations and avocations.

SOME LEARNING CONSIDERATIONS

The nature of this book does not lend itself to a detailed discussion of teaching strategies. For this the reader is referred to other sources.

Children learn mathematics most efficiently only when the right factors converge. Since each individual differs from all others, the learning experiences which prove successful for one child may not succeed with another. The following paragraphs briefly sketch a few important factors relevant to the teaching of elementary school mathematics.

---

[8] For a description of modular arithmetic, see Charles F. Howard and Enoch Dumas, *Teaching Contemporary Mathematics in the Elementary School* (New York: Harper & Row, Publishers, 1966), pp. 80–85.

Curriculum

The items selected for the mathematics curriculum should be relevant to children's needs, interests, and capabilities. To children the need for a feeling of accomplishment and success is important. The mathematical ideas easiest to learn are those which are simply presented, arouse curiosity, and are based on previous learning. After children have learned how to identify sets, they can easily learn how combining (joining) four sets of five items each to show a set of 20 items illustrates $4 \times 5 = 20$.

The content of the mathematics curriculum should facilitate further study, it should be useful in life's activities, and it should increase children's enthusiasm for the subject. Consider, for example, an activity in which a pair of children collect lunch money, multiply $7 \times 45\cent$, and compare the answer with the amount collected. Such an activity might lead to a study of the disposition of the money, what it pays for, and whether or not the hot lunch program is self-supporting or needs to be subsidized.

Sequence

The sequence of presenting topics must be both logical, in the sense that the learner may build his understanding through a continuum from simple to complex, and psychological in the sense that interests may flow from one topic to another. Further, the presentation of items must be consistent with the learner's readiness to profit from instructional activities. The latter condition has given rise to the "spiral approach" to the study of mathematics, wherein one strand or topic, e.g., addition and subtraction, is pursued for a short time and then another strand, e.g., measuring, is undertaken; when all strands suitable to the child's level of development have been partially investigated, the circuit is repeated, each at a slightly more advanced level of sophistication than before.

Teaching procedures

Teaching procedures must be such that children will develop understanding of items before practicing for mastery. Since mathematical ideas are abstract, their learning must be induced through many and varied activities and often employing concrete materials. Some learning takes place through play or even random manipulation of materials followed by a conversation or discussion in which each learner attempts to explain what he has discovered and to compare his ideas with those of others. Play-type activity may be followed by a more structured approach in which the teacher directs activities so that further discoveries emerge. It is here that individual differences become especially apparent to the observant teacher, for some pupils require many more and a greater variety of activities than do others. A frequent teaching error is underestimating how many and how varied the activities need to be before a child has an adequate understanding of concepts. To help the child remember what he has learned, the exploration activities may be followed by such activities as making hypotheses concerning whatever has been explored, further exploration and testing of these hypotheses, and recording or otherwise communicating findings to others. Then a need for practice of steps in a procedure or for automatic recall of facts may follow. In the study of trains suggested previously, children who are exploring the engine may be confronted with the question, "How many gallons of fuel would be required to move a 20-car freight train from New York to Chicago?" Exploration of the problem would lead to guesses or rough estimates, gathering reliable data, calculating, and checking answers against estimates. Then findings may be recorded for use in a final report. The experience may have revealed need for instruction or practice (or both) on multiplying by a two-place multiplier. Even some multiplication facts may need memorization reinforcement. Many boys and girls, especially bright ones, find the typical practice pursuits dull. This book is dedicated to teachers and parents who want to help children maintain interest while they practice for retention.

Materials

The materials of instruction in mathematics must be as diverse as is necessary for effective learning. For example, to use only blocks in teaching the concepts centering around the first ten natural numbers may lead some children to the false notion that number ideas are related only to blocks. Variety of materials has similar importance to variety of activities. Concepts may be more precise when learned through a wide assortment of experiences than when a very limited range is employed. However, it should be pointed out that learning through the use of a very restricted variety of activities and materials is infinitely better than rote learning. Colorful and unusual items often create interests to support a commonplace procedure. Materials used for teaching a mathematical concept may be used also to teach ideas in other curricular areas; e.g., if various kinds of seeds are used to develop a concept of a set as a precisely defined group, one might also use them to lead into a study of science concepts of classification.

Attitudes

The teacher or parent who would help children develop an interest and a competence in mathematics must display certain positive attitudes toward the subject. Paramount among these is enthusiasm. To teach with spirit one must have confidence in his knowledge of the contemporary mathematics on which modern elementary school arithmetic is based.[9] One must believe that mathematics is important to the lives of pupils and that, given the proper instruction, all children can learn some mathematics and some boys and girls can learn a great deal. The effectiveness of a lively teacher can be strengthened by involving children in appropriate and interesting mathematics activities.

---

[9] A good parent-teacher guide is Frances J. Müeller, *Understanding the New Elementary School Mathematics* (Belmont, California: Dickenson Publishing Company, Inc., 1965).

Chapter 2

NUMBERS, NUMERALS, SETS

COUNTING AND NUMBERS

Activities

2–1. To practice numeral recognition and the concept of one more and of one less, distribute number cards to each member of a group. On each card should be a numeral—one to nine or more. Call a number. The pupil with the corresponding number card is invited to stand. His "Neighbors," those with numbers one less and one more, are then invited to join him.

2–2. To provide practice in recognizing the relation of one number to another and in using the appropriate signs when children are familiar with the trichotomy of relations (more than, less than, equal to), place in the hands of each of three pupils a card with a relation sign ($>$, $<$, $=$). When two numbers are called, the two children having the appropriate number cards come to the front of the room and the person having the correct relation card comes to stand between them.

2–3. To draw attention to the practical applications of number systems, carry out a discussion and listing of activities or vocations requiring the use of various number systems: natural, whole, rational, and real. If the teacher and pupils are sufficiently sophisticated, do the same with the complex number system. Examples:

Number System	Activity	Vocation
Natural numbers	Counting cattle	Cattle raising
Whole numbers	Score keeping	Baseball playing
Rational numbers	Selling meat	Meat cutting
Real numbers	Adjusting an odometer	Mechanical engineering
Complex numbers	Calculating the output of a dynamo	Electrical engineering

Materials

2–4. To facilitate teaching counting, ordinal numbers, place value, sets, and concepts of addition and subtraction, gather several hundred small, interesting, non-rolling items such as eucalytus pods, bottle caps, acorns, maple seeds, sea shells, small flat stones, miniature toys, or the like. Some things can be painted or otherwise colored brightly. (For very young children, avoid toxic paints.)

When teaching counting, items may be moved from one pile to another one at a time and while saying the numbers. This will help to establish the habit of associating one number name with each item moved. Children need to learn that the number of the last item touched tells the number of the set.

A set of items lined up in a row may be used to identify the first, second, third, etc.

By grouping a pile of things in sets of ten, one can promote an understanding of the principle of place value as applied to a numeration system. The number 23 would be represented by two sets of ten items and a set of three.

Depending on the variety of attributes among the items, one can help children select sets with given properties, e.g., a set of seeds or a set of red, round objects.

For teaching addition and subtraction, sets of varying number may be joined or separated.

2–5. To teach an understanding of number values, make strips of heavy paper in a way such that each is one inch longer than the one before it. Mark the appropriate numeral on each strip.

2–6. Practice in counting can be achieved through the use of clean plastic pill boxes (obtainable from a pharmacy) in which varying numbers of small objects such as corn, beans, peas, peanuts, paper clips, brass fasteners, buttons are placed. Children are to count the objects in each box and place the boxes in order by numbers, or they may record the numbers on a sheet of paper.

Variation: Write a numeral on each of several pill boxes. Children may place the appropriate number of small objects in each box. The objects may be different from each other to avoid developing a concept of number as being related only to things of the same kind.

2–7. A common wire clothes hanger and a handful of clothespins can be used when teaching counting and when showing sets and subsets (useful in teaching addition and subtraction facts).

Large wooden beads or button molds strung on a wire can be used similarly.

2–8. The directions that follow are for making materials to use in the same way one might use Cuisenaire rods,[1] but related to English rather than metric measurement units. Using a fine-tooth saw, cut a 1″ x 1″ board into pieces of varying length; the smallest should be one inch long and each additional piece an inch longer than the one before it until a piece ten inches long is

Length (Inches)	Color	Number of pieces
1	white	10
2	light red	8
3	light green	6
4	dark red or purple	5
5	yellow	4
6	dark green	4
7	black	3
8	brown	3
9	blue	2
10	orange	2

[1] Information about Cuisenaire rods may be obtained from Cuisenaire Company of America, Inc., 12 Church Street, New Rochelle, New York 10805. Numerous games using cuisenaire rods are found under appropriate topics throughout this book.

made. How many are needed depends on the number of children to be served. For one or two children at a time the following set may be large enough. Paint or color as indicated using paint, dye, or crayon.

Use for demonstration or for one or two pupils, following the directions for Cuisenaire rods.

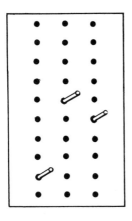

2–9. To illustrate the value of decimally represented numbers, make a peg-type abacus. Select a board 1″ x 6″ x 10″; drill ¼″ holes in three rows one inch apart to represent ones, tens, and hundreds. Make three short loose-fitting pieces of doweling to use as pegs. The illustration at left shows how the number 265 would be represented. Use as you would an abacus. (If this device is used with beginners, more pegs should be made so that they may be used as are the beads on an abacus. Thus, for the number 265, two pegs would be placed in the hundreds column, six in the tens column, and five in the ones column.)

2–10. To teach number representations, make for each child a simple abacus of heavy cardboard, elastic string, and short macaroni pieces soaked in food coloring. With yours as a model, help children make their own. Knots are tied on the back. Because of the elastic, spare pieces can be brought to the front if one is

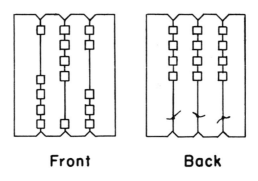

Front   **Back**

broken. Also it is easy to have only as many beads in front as are needed for the numeral base being illustrated.

Bulletin boards

2–11. To encourage counting at the kindergarten or first grade level, cut out stars (or other interesting designs) and pin them in a random pattern on the bulletin board. Label, "How Many Stars Today?" If children have learned how to write numerals, post a scratch pad, pencil, and envelope at the base of the bulletin board. Change the number of stars daily.

2–12. To follow a presentation of prime numbers and how to locate them, make a bulletin board titled "Prime Numbers," showing an example of the Sieve of Eratosthenes. (See number 2-13 below.)

History

2–13. Sieve of Eratosthenes. (to recreate an early scheme for locating prime numbers) A Greek mathematician, Eratosthenes, devised a method of determining prime numbers which became known as the Sieve of Eratosthenes.[2] Essentially, it consisted of crossing out all multiples of each prime number as it was located. All remaining numbers were primes (except the number one, which is neither a prime nor a composite number).

$$1 \quad 2 \quad 3 \quad \cancel{4} \quad 5 \quad \cancel{6} \quad 7 \quad \cancel{8} \quad \cancel{9} \quad \cancel{10}$$
$$11 \quad \cancel{12} \quad 13 \quad \cancel{14} \quad \cancel{15} \quad \cancel{16} \quad 17 \quad \cancel{18} \quad 19 \quad \cancel{20}$$
$$\cancel{21} \quad \cancel{22} \quad \cdots$$

Games

2–14. Counting Party. PURPOSE: to provide practice in counting.

---

[2] See Francis J. Mueller, *Arithmetic: Its Structure and Concepts* (Englewood Cliffs, N.J.: Prentice-Hall, Inc., 1965), pp. 193–195.

LEVEL: K to 1.

NUMBER OF PLAYERS: 4 or more.

MATERIALS NEEDED: None.

PROCEDURE: Give each player a number name. Select a party host or hostess who sits in a corner of the room. Each player in turn goes to the corner and knocks on the wall as many times as indicated by his number name. The host or hostess says, "Hello. Is your name _____?" If the guest says, "Yes, my name is _____," his reply indicates that he knocked correctly, and that the host counted correctly; so the host says, "Then you may come to my party." The guest then sits in the corner and helps the host or hostess count the knocks of other guests. If the guest makes a mistake, he is told, "You were not invited." And he must go back; he may try again after all others have had a turn. If the host makes a mistake, he is replaced by the guest.

2–15. Finger Count. PURPOSE: to provide practice in counting.

LEVEL: K to 1.

NUMBER OF PLAYERS: 2 or more.

MATERIALS NEEDED: None.

PROCEDURE: Seat players in a semicircle. Have children repeat with you:

> Fish, cats, puppies, look at me.
> How many fingers do you see?

Hold up one or both hands with a selected number of fingers raised and call on a child to tell you. If he is correct, praise him; if not correct, help him count the raised fingers.

2–16. Taps. PURPOSE: to provide practice in counting and in making one-to-one correspondences.

LEVEL: K to 1.

NUMBER OF PLAYERS: 1 or more.

MATERIALS NEEDED: Beans or other markers.

PROCEDURE: Distribute a number of markers to each player with instructions to lay out as many as he hears tapped when you strike a table with a pencil or ruler. Check quickly and have each child return his markers to his pile so as to be ready for the next series of taps.

2–17. Trick-or-Treat. PURPOSE: to provide practice in counting and experience with the language associated with the operation of subtraction.

LEVEL: K to 1.

NUMBER OF PLAYERS: 2 or more.

MATERIALS NEEDED: Small objects such as seeds or plastic discs.

PROCEDURE: To each player distribute a selected number of objects. The leader carries a paper bag and knocks on the "door" (desk) of a player and asks for a certain number of items which must be counted. The person visited must also tell how many objects he has left. If correct, the visitor moves on to another place.

2–18. Hot or Cold. PURPOSE: to provide practice in recognizing the relative position of a given number to other numbers and experience in reading numerals.

LEVEL: K to 1.

NUMBER OF PLAYERS: 2 or more.

MATERIALS NEEDED: Number line and pointer.

PROCEDURE: Select a child to be "It." He "hides his eyes" while another child points to a numeral on the number line. When all players except "It" have noted which numeral was selected, "It" may uncover his eyes and guess the "burning" number. The leader gives "It" hints by saying "cold" if the guess is far off the mark, "hot" if he is close, and "burning" when he guesses correctly. Repeat with other leaders and guessers.

2–19. Circle Sets. PURPOSE: to provide practice in recognizing the value of numbers.

LEVEL: K to 1.

NUMBER OF PLAYERS: 10 or more.

MATERIALS NEEDED: None.

PROCEDURE: Arrange players in a circle. Call out a number, e.g., "Four. Begin with Mary." Children then form themselves into sets of four with leftover players dropping out. The sets of children circle clockwise. At a signal, all stop and those who dropped out rejoin the circle. Call another number and a new starting place.

    Circle Sets could be adapted to provide practice in reading

numerals by having the teacher show a numeral rather than calling it out.

2–20. Circus. PURPOSE: to provide practice in recognizing a numeral and its number value.

LEVEL: K to 1.

NUMBER OF PLAYERS: 2 or more.

MATERIALS NEEDED: Cards on each of which is a numeral.

PROCEDURE: Distribute cards, one to each player. Select a ringmaster and then have the other pupils stand in a circle and pretend they are trained circus ponies. When the ringmaster calls a number, the pony who has the appropriate card steps to the center of the ring and taps his foot as many times as the number indicates. If he is correct, the ringmaster permits the pony to run once around the circle.

2–21. Mischievous Kitten. PURPOSE: to provide practice in recognizing number words and corresponding number values.

LEVEL: K to 1.

NUMBER OF PLAYERS: 1 or more.

MATERIALS NEEDED: Vocabulary cards containing number words or ordinal words.

PROCEDURE: Place word cards at random in the chalk tray. Ask pupils to say each word with you. Then ask children to help you place them in correct sequence. Next, say that while children "hide their eyes" a mischievous kitten will come and change the order of the cards. Children cover eyes and lower heads to desk or laps. Teacher switches cards and then calls on a pupil to return them to the correct places. Repeat with a child as the mischievous kitten.

2–22. Loading the Steps. PURPOSE: to provide experience in discovering relationships.

LEVEL: K to 1.

NUMBER OF PLAYERS: 1 or more.

MATERIALS USED: Cuisenaire rods.[3]

---

3 See number 2–8.

PROCEDURE: Players are asked to select the smallest rod, then add other rods to form steps—white, red, green, purple, etc. Leader then asks, "Who can find rods to place on each step to make all steps as high as the orange step?" Then, "Who can name the rods used??" (White and blue, red and brown, green and black, etc.) "Can anyone close his eyes and tell me the rods placed on each step?"

VARIATION: Select a rod other than the orange one and follow same procedure as above. Then ask players to remove the rod placed on each step. See who can name the rod which must be placed on each step to match a given step (without manipulating rods).

2–23. Match It. PURPOSE: to provide experience in discovering relationships.

LEVEL: K to 1.

NUMBER OF PLAYERS: 1 or more.

MATERIALS NEEDED: Cuisenaire rods.[4]

PROCEDURE: Select the orange rod. Ask players to find how many red rods are needed to match the long one. Do the same with blue; can it be done? "Who can find *all* the rods which can be matched by red ones placed end to end?" (For example, two red ones end to end are matched by a purple one.) Do the same with green, purple, and yellow rods. See if anyone can find two rods of the same color to measure the same as the black one; the yellow one.

2–24. Trains. PURPOSE: to provide experience in matching, in counting, and in seeing relationships.

LEVEL: K to 1.

NUMBER OF PLAYERS: 1 or more.

MATERIALS NEEDED: Cuisenaire rods.[5]

PROCEDURE: Ask players to make a "train'" of three red rods. "How many green ones will make a train measuring the same length?" Make the red train longer and see how many green rods are needed to match the length, and which red trains can not be

---

[4] See number 2–8.

[5] See number 2–8.

matched with green ones. Follow by matching various series of red rods with trains of other rods; see if children can tell which red trains cannot be matched by series of each color.

VARIATION: Make train of a color other than red and then follow above procedure.

2–25. Rod Numbers. PURPOSE: to provide experience in matching, in counting, and in seeing relationships.

LEVEL: K to 2.

NUMBER OF PLAYERS: 1 or more.

MATERIALS NEEDED: Cuisenaire rods.[6]

PROCEDURE: Ask players to call the white rod, one. Then find number names for each color by checking to see how many white rods are needed to measure the same as each other rod.

Now find how many combinations of rods named by their number names can be found to match a given rod, also named by number, e.g., five (yellow): 4 and 1; 3 and 2; 2, 2, and 1; 1, 1, 1, and 2; etc. See who has found most matching series. Change base rod and proceed as before.

If Rod Numbers is played orally, children might describe their findings in words before using equations, i.e., four red rods and one green rod are the same length as one yellow rod. If children can write, they should be encouraged to record their findings like this, "4 red rods and 1 green rod are the same length as 1 yellow rod;" later, like this, "4 R and 1 G are the same length as 1 Y."

VARIATION: When players get proficient at the above game, see if they can play it by writing down the numbers of each series without manipulating rods. Plus signs may be used, as $3 + 1 + 1 = 5$. If a series named by one player is challenged by another, rods may be used to check.

2–26. Same As. PURPOSE: to provide experience in finding relationships.

LEVEL: K to 2.

NUMBER OF PLAYERS: 2 or more.

MATERIALS NEEDED: A set of Cuisenaire rods[7] for each player.

---

[6] See number 2–8.

[7] See number 2–8.

PROCEDURE: Players spread rods before them. Leader asks pupils to find as many combinations of rods as they can to match a given rod or combination of rods, e.g., orange rod, blue and yellow rods, or two dark green rods. When nearly all have finished, call time and ask what discoveries have been made. Children can then be asked to record their findings in their math notebooks or the teacher can record their oral reports. Repeat the play with some other standard.

VARIATION: Ask players to join end to end two, three, four, or more rods. Then see who can find the fewest rods to match the length of the first series.

2–27. Stairsteps. PURPOSE: to provide practice in naming Cuisenaire rods when they are arranged in order of relative lengths.

LEVEL: K to 2.

NUMBER OF PLAYERS: 1 or more.

MATERIALS NEEDED: Cuisenaire rods.[8]

PROCEDURE: Leader asks players to select the smallest rod, then add other rods to form steps—white, red, green, purple, etc. Ask pupils, one at a time, to "go up the stairs" by naming the rods from smallest to largest, then "go downstairs" by naming from largest to smallest. Follow with, "Who can go up the stairs and down again with eyes shut?"

A teaching activity to follow the playing of Stairsteps might lead children to discover the "one more" principle of natural numbers. One way to do this is by numbering the rods from one to ten beginning with the white one, and then asking children how many white rods need to be added to the white step to make it the height of the red one, how many white rods are needed to make the red one the same height as the light green one, and so on.

2–28. Jump Board. PURPOSE: to provide practice in a variety of counting activities and in reading and following directions.

LEVEL: 1 to 3.

NUMBER OF PLAYERS: 2.

[8] See number 2–8.

MATERIALS NEEDED: A playing board about a foot square with circle stepping stones numbered from one to 100. Two buttons or other markers. A set of direction cards, e.g., make two jumps by three's. Make five jumps by two's. Go back to one. Jump to 100 and win. Go back three jumps by four's.

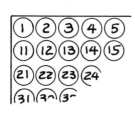

PROCEDURE: Shuffle cards and place face down. Players take turns drawing cards and following the directions. Winner is the one who gets to 100 first. Note: If a player gets a card which would take him farther back than one, he moves only to one.

2–29. Buzz. PURPOSE: to provide practice in counting and in giving recognition to numbers with certain characteristics.

LEVEL: 1 to 6.

NUMBER OF PLAYERS: 2 or more.

MATERIALS NEEDED: None.

PROCEDURE: Players form a circle. Vary directions according to ability of players. First and second graders might count by turns except that when a given digit is part of a numeral the person whose turn it is says, "Buzz;" e.g., if the digit is three: 1, 2, buzz, 4, 5, . . . 12, buzz, 14, 15, . . . At grade three, "buzz" may be substituted for all even numbers; at fourth and fifth grades, all multiples of four; at sixth grade, all multiples of six and all numerals in which the digit six occurs (6, 12, 16, . . .), or all multiples of four and seven—"buzz" for the former and "tizz" for the latter. If a number is a multiple of both four and seven, say "buzz, tizz." Vary the selection of digits.

2–30. Which Was It? PURPOSE: to provide practice in recalling relationships among rods.

LEVEL: 1 to 3.

NUMBER OF PLAYERS: 1 or more.

MATERIALS NEEDED: Cuisenaire rods.[9]

PROCEDURE: Ask each player to select one rod, e.g., black, and then make all the patterns of other blocks which show the same

---

[9] See number 2–8.

length (purple and light green; white, red, light green; etc.). Now have each player remove the right-hand rod of his pattern, placing it out of sight. Then see who can replace rods correctly by picking up the right one with no fumbling. Follow with removing left-hand rod. Then same procedure beginning with a different rod.

VARIATION: Assign numbers to rods. Then duplicate papers showing number patterns with variable at right or left. Players are to fill in missing numerals, such as $7 = (4 + 2) + \square$ or $7 = \square + (2 + 1)$. Players may check, using Cuisenaire rods whenever necessary.

2–31. Cuisenaire Rummy. PURPOSE: to provide practice in recalling the relationships among Cuisenaire rods[10] regardless of what number is assigned a given rod.

LEVEL: 1 to 4.

NUMBER OF PLAYERS: 2 to 4.

MATERIALS NEEDED: Set of cards colored as indicated.

CARDS: ten whites, nine reds, seven light greens, six purples, five yellows, four dark greens, three blacks, three browns, three blues, two oranges.

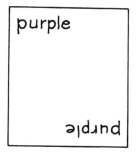

PROCEDURE: Deal five cards to each player. Place balance of deck face down on table except for top card which should be turned up and placed beside the others. Player to left of dealer begins by laying before him "books" of three cards such that the lengths of rods represented by two of the cards measures the same as the rod named on the third card, e.g., G (light green) and K (black) measures the same length as O (orange). Player may draw one card—either the one turned up or the top card on the "blind" deck; when he has completed play, he must discard one card face up (unless he can use the last card to complete a book). The first to play all cards in his hand says, "Rummy." Score is calculated by adding the values of all books (assigning a unit value to white and giving a book the value of the longest rod represented) and subtracting the value of each card remaining in a player's hand.

---

[10] See number 2–8.

2–32. Two Words. PURPOSE: to provide advanced pupils with practice in recognizing perfect squares and multiples of selected numbers.

LEVEL: 3 to 6.

NUMBER OF PLAYERS: 2 or more.

MATERIALS NEEDED: None.

PROCEDURE: Select two words, mathematical or otherwise, e.g., "plus" and "minus." Designate some ordering of the pupils in the room, and decide on some number, preferably in the range three through nine. Suppose, for example, seven is chosen. The players, in turn, are then to say the number names in order. The exceptions are that when the number is a perfect square (as 1, 4, 9, 16, etc.) the pupil is to say "plus" instead of the number word, and when the number is a multiple of seven (as 7, 14, 21, etc.) the pupil is to say "minus" instead of the number word. Example: plus (since 1 is a square), two, three, plus (since 4 is a square), five, six, minus, eight, etc. Play proceeds until the first "plus-minus" number is reached, which will be the square of the number chosen (49 in the case of 7). Whenever a mistake is made by a player, the sequence is ended and a new start made with the next pupil. The one who finally completes the sequence with "plus-minus" may be declared the winner.

Verses (To add the pleasure of rhyme to counting practice).

2–33.   One, two, three, four, five;
            Watch my big seal dive.
            Six, seven, eight, nine, ten;
            There he goes again.

2–34.   One for the money,
            Two for the show,
            Three to make ready,
            And four to go.

2–35.   One, two, tie your shoe;
            Three, four, close the door;
            Five, six, pick up sticks;
            Seven, eight, lay them straight;
            Nine, ten, a big fat hen.

2–36. One, two, three, four, five,
Catching fishes all alive.
"Why did you let them go?"
"Because they bit my finger so."
"Which finger did they bite?"
"The little finger on the right."[11]

2–37. 1, 2, 3, 4, 5,
I caught a bird alive;
6, 7, 8, 9, 10,
I let him go again.

2–37. Jump Rope Rhymes.

Brother, brother, help me, do,
Pick up sticks and kindling too,
If we work, the pile will grow;
Come, let's count them row by row:
1, 2, 3, 4, 5, 6, 7, 8, 9, 10.[12]

2–39. Fireman, fireman, we can't wait;
There's a fire in apartment Eight.
Up the stairs he'll drag the hose;
Count the steps as up he goes—
1, 2, 3, 4, 5, 6, 7, 8, 9, 10.[13]

2–40. A Birthday Verse.

"Today, today," the big clock ticks,
"Kathleen is six, Kathleen is six!

It seems but no time, sakes alive,
Since she was five, since she was five.

And only minutes, nothing more,
Since she was four, since she was four.

Tick, tock, tick, tock, How can it be
That Kathleen Ann is two times three?

Such funny things she used to do
When she was two, when she was two.

Tick, tock, how fast the hours have run,

---

[11] John R. Clark, Charlotte W. Junge, and Carolyn H. Clark, *Let's Count* (New York: Harcourt, Brace and World, Inc., 1962), p. T15.

[12] *Ibid.*, p. T2.

[13] *Ibid.*

Since she was one, since she was one.
And now she's half of twelve! So quick
The birthdays fly! Tock, tick, tock, tick,
Kathleen is six, Kathleen is six,
Hurray! Hurray," the big clock ticks.[14]

INTEGERS

Materials

2–41. To represent integers visually, use red and black checkers
—a red checker for minus one, and a black checker for plus one.
Then, a set of six red checkers and three black ones could represent the number minus three.

Other materials also can be used to represent positive and
negative numbers: a ladder, part of which is under water, with
numbers assigned to rungs; beads on a wire frame with a ribbon
divider; money and IOU's; a thermometer showing degrees above
and below zero; and others, some of which might be suggested by
pupils.

Games

2–42. Out of the Red. PURPOSE: to provide practice in adding
integers.

LEVEL: 3 to 6.

NUMBER OF PLAYERS: 2 or more.

MATERIALS NEEDED: Spinner and dial. Numerals for negative
numbers are red and for positive numbers are black.

PROCEDURE: Divide group into two teams or, if group is small,
play as individuals. Players take turns spinning twice. Add numbers for score; red numerals represent negative integers, black
represent positive integers. After each individual has had several
turns or all members of each team have had turns, total the scores.
Some scores may be negative, "in the red."

For pupils sophisticated in manipulating integers, numbers
may be subtracted or multiplied.

---

[14] Author Unknown.

2–43. Stay Out of the Hole. PURPOSE: to provide practice in adding integers.

LEVEL: 3 to 6.

NUMBER OF PLAYERS: 2 or more.

MATERIALS NEEDED: A cardboard or plywood grid 24″ x 24″ with four-inch squares. In each square write the numeral for an integer. Three small bean bags.

PROCEDURE: If group is large, divide into teams; if small, play as individuals. Select an umpire. Place grid on floor at a distance from a chalk mark appropriate to the maturity of the players, four to ten feet. Each player tosses three bean bags onto the grid. His score will be the total of the numbered squares on which the bags stop.

⁻14	⁻12	⁻4	⁻2	⁻10	⁻16
⁻8	⁺12	⁺7	⁺9	⁺13	⁻6
⁺1	⁺3	⁺18	⁺15	⁺6	0
⁻1	⁺5	⁺16	⁺17	⁺4	⁺2
⁻7	⁺14	⁺10	⁺8	⁺11	⁻9
⁻17	⁻11	⁺3	⁻5	⁻13	⁻15

The umpire gives the player the higher of two scores if there is doubt. Players must add their scores. Note that it is possible to have a negative score.

NUMBER LINE

Activity

2–44. To add meaning to numbers, buy some rolls of common adding machine tape. Start making a number line on one by marking short vertical lines at one-inch intervals and numbering, 1, 2, 3, . . . If a child shows interest, let him continue the process. Others might "spell him off" if he tires, or he may want to take it home to work on. When much has been done, let children (especially including the one, or ones, who did the marking) help stretch the tape around the room (and down the hall if necessary). Fasten with masking tape for easy removal. Let pupils explore the number line to find numbers of interest to them.

Discuss other kinds of number lines (by twos, by tens, by doubling, or by halving intervals, etc.). If any children show interest, permit them to experiment with tapes.

Materials

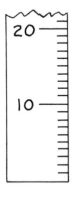

2–45. To increase children's versatility in using number lines, make some that are different from the common horizontal variety frequently shown in textbooks or drawn on the chalkboard. One such number line may be made by fastening together strips of tagboard, 2″ to 4″ wide, end to end, to make a single strip 4′ 2″ long. Mark at ½″ intervals with heavy marks after every ten intervals. Mount vertically. Do not overlook the possibility that children might make their own number lines. One way is for them to fold strips of paper and then number the folds.

Games

2–46. Number Line Hop. PURPOSE: to use the number line for addition and subtraction of directed numbers.

LEVEL: K to 3.

NUMBER OF PLAYERS: 2 or more.

MATERIALS NEEDED: A large number line drawing on the playground. Make unit marks about 18 inches apart. Use either whole numbers or integers depending on what has been taught.

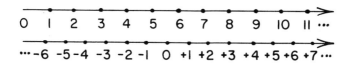

PROCEDURE: Divide group into two teams. The first player of one team gives three directions to the first player of the second team, e.g., "Begin on negative three; hop four spaces to the right; hop two more to the right; now hop three spaces to the left. Where are you?" If the hopper answers correctly, he may call directions to the first player on the first team; if not, he must drop out and wait for the next game. In the latter case, the second player of the second team does the calling. When all have had a turn, see which team has the most players still in the game.

VARIATIONS: (1) Young children for whom hopping is difficult may step off spaces. (2) Instead of instructions to hop right and left, ask players to add positive or negative integers.

2–47. Kangaroo Jump. PURPOSE: to use the number line for adding and subtracting integers, or for counting by two's or three's, or for multiplying.

LEVEL: 1 to 2.

NUMBER OF PLAYERS: An arithmetic group.

MATERIALS NEEDED: Chalk and chalkboard.

PROCEDURE: Draw a picture of a number line on the chalkboard. Nearby place a picture of a kangaroo (or grasshopper or frog). Call on a child to come to the board and show how the kangaroo jumps along the number line. "He starts at zero and jumps two spaces to the right, then four more, then three more. Now where is the kangaroo?" Vary the game as desired, e.g., for subtraction the kangaroo might take seven jumps to the right and then four jumps to the left; for counting by two's or multiplying, the jumps may be all of a given length. If desired, the kangaroo might jump from the right of zero to the left of zero into the land of negative numbers.

NUMERALS

Activities

2–48. To provide practice in recognizing numerals and their sequence when counting, distribute number cards to each member of the group. On each card should be a numeral—one to nine at first, later 11 and up. Suggest that, in turn, children place their cards in the chalk tray in proper sequence.

2–49. For practice in writing numerals for large numbers, suggest that children write a numeral for a number larger than 5000; between 150,000 and 300,000; less than 1,000,000 but greater than 500,000; greater than 10,000 but containing no zeros; and so on.

2–50. To provide an activity in which numerals do not represent numbers, suggest that children make up a code which substitutes numerals for letters. Then write short messages for others to decode. (The simplest such code assigns natural numbers to the letters, as 1,a; 2,b; 3,c; etc.)

Materials

2–51. When teaching numerals and their meanings, place in a pocket chart cards on which numerals appear. Permit a child to match each card with one on which semi-concrete representations appear (as dots in domino arrangements) or basic facts.

2–52. Some children need tactile reinforcement in order to learn to recognize or to write numerals. Try cards on which sandpaper numerals have been glued. (Do not use your best scissors!)

Touch sensations can be varied through choice of materials. Sandpaper comes in many grades, from very fine to very coarse. Flocked paper or cloth such as felt, velvet, canvas, or worsted wool provides further choices.

2–53. When teaching the recognition of numerals, their sequence when counting, and their number values, make a board 25″ x 3″ marked off in 2½″ rectangles. Paste slips of papers in each section showing numerals 1 to 10. Drive two small nails near the lower edge of each division. Place in the chalk tray or hang at an easy level for kindergarten children. Make cards 2″ x 3″ with holes punched to correspond to nails. Pupils match cards until they know the sequence; then pictures showing semi-concrete representations should be substituted for the numerals on the board.

1	2	3	4	5	6	7	8	9	10

2–54. To give practice in learning the natural number sequence, make a simple outline of an animal such as a cat, or other familiar object, on a piece of paper. Then, using a duplicator carbon, write on the outline the 15 to 25 numerals on which recognition practice is needed. Run off copies. Suggest that pupils draw lines from one numeral to the next, beginning with the one representing the least number and progressing to the greatest.

The result should be the outline with which you started. See also numbers 2–8, 2–9, and 7–12.

Charts

2–55. A chart for showing numerals from 0 to 100 by tens is useful to supplement pocket charts, number lines, and other graphic devices for relating the decimal numeration system to the system of whole numbers. For some purposes, a chart of natural numbers may be useful. It may be made with the zero as in Chart B or as in Chart A. For more on charts, see numbers 2–89 and 2–90.

Whole Numbers									
One Hundred									
0	1	2	3	4	5	6	7	8	9
10	11	12	13	14	15	16	17	18	19
20	21	22	23	24	25	26	27	28	29
30	31	32	33	34	35	36	37	38	39
40	41	42	43	44	45	46	47	48	49
50	51	52	53	54	55	56	57	58	59
60	61	62	63	64	65	66	67	68	69
70	71	72	73	74	75	76	77	78	79
80	81	82	83	84	85	86	87	88	89
90	91	92	93	94	95	96	97	98	99
100									

CHART A

Natural Numbers									
One Hundred									
1	2	3	4	5	6	7	8	9	10
11	12	13	14	15	16	17	18	19	20
21	22	23	24	25	26	27	28	29	30
31	32	33	34	35	36	37	38	39	40
41	42	43	44	45	46	47	48	49	50
51	52	53	54	55	56	57	58	59	60
61	62	63	64	65	66	67	68	69	70
71	72	73	74	75	76	77	78	79	80
81	82	83	84	85	86	87	88	89	90
91	92	93	94	95	96	97	98	99	100

CHART B

Games

2–56. Tune My TV. PURPOSE: to give practice in associating numbers and numerals.

LEVELS: K to 1.

NUMBER OF PLAYERS: 2 or more.

MATERIALS NEEDED: An outline of a TV set on the chalkboard.

PROCEDURE: Invite a player to come to the board to "tune" the TV by writing a channel number. He says, "I have selected Channel ____." If his statement corresponds to what he has written, he may choose the next player.

VARIATION: For more advanced pupils, have them write on the "screen" as many combinations as they can, the answer to which is the channel number. Include those operations which the children can manage—addition, subtraction, multiplication, or division.

2–57. Number Bingo. PURPOSE: to give practice in recognizing numerals.

LEVEL: K to 1.

NUMBER OF PLAYERS: 2 or more.

MATERIALS NEEDED: Duplicated grids. Flat beans or other markers.

PROCEDURE: Help children choose a five-letter word or name, perhaps a child's (all different letters), and write it in the top area. Select five digits on which practice is needed and suggest that the series be written in the squares under each letter in whatever order appeals to a child. (For beginners, prepare the playing boards in advance.) Call letters and numbers at random, as "N, 8." Pupils place beans on proper digits. The leader must keep a record of what has been called by writing numerals called on a card of his own. (Leader's card is blank except for name at top.) When a player has five in a row either vertically or horizontally, he calls, "Giant," or whatever word is on the card. He is the winner.

G	I	A	N	T
7	5	4	8	6
6	7	5	4	8
8	4	7	6	5
4	6	6	7	4
5	8	8	5	7

2–58. Partners. PURPOSE: to provide practice in recognizing numerals.

LEVEL: K to 1.

NUMBER OF PLAYERS: 4 or more.

MATERIALS NEEDED: Two sets of cards—one with numerals and one with corresponding pictures of sets·

PROCEDURE: Distribute cards among players. Select a player to come to the front, to show his card, and to say, "Who will be my partner?" The one who has the corresponding card will join the first player. All check to see if the pairing is correct; if it is, the second player may call on the next one.

2–59. Pocket Match. PURPOSE: to provide practice in recognizing numerals and associating cardinal numbers.

LEVEL: K to 1.

NUMBER OF PLAYERS: 1 or more.

MATERIALS NEEDED: Pocket chart. Two sets of cards, one with numerals and one with pictures of sets of objects.

PROCEDURE: Players take turns placing numeral cards in pocket chart in proper order. Then continue turns as they place pictures over corresponding numerals indicating the number property of the sets.

2–60. Dots and Numbers. PURPOSE: to provide practice in recognizing numerals and associating cardinal numbers.

LEVEL: K to 1.

NUMBER OF PLAYERS: 2 or more.

MATERIALS NEEDED: Two sets of cards—on one set write numerals on which children need practice and on the other show spots in characteristic patterns.

PROCEDURE: Place the numeral cards face down in a box and place the corresponding pattern cards in the chalk tray. Call on a child to get a card from the box and place it over the equivalent card in the chalk tray. If correct, the child may choose the next player.

2–61. Race to Uncle Jack's House. PURPOSE: to provide practice in recognizing numerals and their number values.

LEVEL: K to 1.

NUMBER OF PLAYERS: 2 to 4.

MATERIALS NEEDED: A playing board with a route from home to Uncle Jack's shown in a chain of 40 squares. Tiny cars (paper will do) of different colors, one for each player. A set of 50 cards on each of which is a numeral from 0 to 9.

PROCEDURE: Shuffle cards and place them face down. Each player selects a car. In turn, each child draws a card and moves his car as many squares as the numeral indicates. The first one who gets to Uncle Jack's house wins.

2–62. My Neighbors. PURPOSE: to provide practice in applying the concepts of "one more than" and "one less than," and in writing numerals.

LEVEL: K to 1.

NUMBER OF PLAYERS: 2 or more.

MATERIALS NEEDED: Chalk and chalkboard.

PROCEDURE: Write a numeral on the chalkboard and say, "I am 28. Who can write the names of my neighbors?" Call on a child who will write the numerals 27 and 29 on either side of your 28. Continue with other numbers on which the children need practice.

2–63. Match Me. PURPOSE: to provide practice in recognizing numerals and their number values.

LEVEL: K to 1.

NUMBER OF PLAYERS: 4 or more.

MATERIALS NEEDED: A set of cards consisting of subsets of three —one set with numerals, another with corresponding number words, and the third with spots in characteristic pattern to show how many.

PROCEDURE: Distribute cards among players (some may have more than one card). Call on a child to come before the group and tell the number his card indicates. He says, "Who can match me?" Players with corresponding cards come to front and stand beside the first. All hold cards in full view of other players. If the latter agree that the cards match, the trio return to their seats. The first child called on now selects the next player.

VARIATION: Play a simple variety of rummy. Use two sets of cards. The cards may be dealt one at a time until each player has six. The rest of the deck is placed face down on the playing surface; the top card is turned face up beside the deck (this will be the discard pile). The object of the game is to meld (lay down, face up) sets of three matching cards. Each player in turn draws one top card either from the deck or from the discard pile. If he can meld, he does so and then discards one card. When a player discards his last card, the game is over. Score may, be the number of cards left in each player's hand; low score wins.

2–64. General Delivery. PURPOSE: to provide practice in recognizing numerals and their names.

LEVEL: K to 1.

NUMBER OF PLAYERS: 2 or more.

MATERIALS NEEDED: Cards about the size of letter envelopes, on each side of which is a numeral children need to practice reading. A facsimile of a postoffice.

PROCEDURE: Select a Postmaster and give him a set of "letters." Other players line up at the postoffice and as each gets to the window he asks, "Is there any mail for me?" The Postmaster selects a letter and says, "Is this your name?" If the player correctly reads the numeral on the letter he says, "Yes, my name is ____," and takes his letter to his "home."

2–65. Number Match. PURPOSE: to provide practice in recognizing number words.

LEVEL: 1 to 2.

NUMBER OF PLAYERS: 2 or more.

MATERIALS NEEDED: Two sets of cards—on one write Hindu-Arabic numerals and on the other write number names. Select those on which players need practice.

PROCEDURE: Place cards on which Hindu-Arabic numerals are marked in the chalk tray. Place the other cards in a paper bag. Divide group into teams, each to alternate in sending a player to take a card from the paper bag and match it with the proper one in the chalk tray. One point is scored for each successful pairing. The team with most points at the end of play wins. If the group is large, return cards to their places from time to time; mix the cards in the paper bag.

Number Match may be played non-competitively. Children take turns drawing a card from the paper bag and matching it with its mate in the chalk tray.

2–66. Numeral Race. PURPOSE: to provide practice in recognizing numerals.

LEVEL: 1 to 4.

NUMBER OF PLAYERS: 4 to 20.

MATERIALS NEEDED: Two sets of 3″ x 5″ (or larger) cards, a card in each set showing a digit, 0 to 9. (Games to show decimal numerals require two additional cards, each with a decimal point.)

PROCEDURE: Select teams and distribute cards so that each team has one card for each of numerals 0 to 9. Teacher or leader reads a numeral and pupils race to see which team can get to the front of the room first and line up with correct cards for the numeral given. For example, if the numeral is 10, cards 1 and 0 must line up. After five plays, team members exchange cards.

Likely to be a noisy game.

2–67. Rationalo. PURPOSE: to provide practice in recognizing a variety of numerals to name certain numbers.

LEVEL: 4 to 6.

NUMBER OF PLAYERS: 2 to 4.

MATERIALS NEEDED: A set of 52 cards containing 13 sets of cards on which given rational numbers are shown as four different numerals, e.g.,

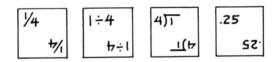

Suggested numbers are $\frac{1}{2}$, $\frac{1}{3}$, $\frac{2}{3}$, $\frac{1}{4}$, $\frac{3}{4}$, $\frac{1}{5}$, $\frac{2}{5}$, $\frac{3}{5}$, $\frac{4}{5}$, $\frac{1}{8}$, $\frac{3}{8}$, $\frac{5}{8}$, $\frac{7}{8}$. If desired, two sets of cards may be made—one with numerals easy to recognize and one with numerals more difficult.

PROCEDURE: Dealer distributes five cards to each player. Balance of deck is placed face down at center of table with one card turned up. Player to left of dealer begins by drawing one card, either the turned-up one or one from the top of the blind deck. He then tries to find a set of four cards each showing the same number regardless of form of numeral. If he cannot, he discards one card and play goes to next person who may take one or all discards or draw one from blind deck. Play ends when one player has a set. He scores one point. Cards are shuffled and game continues with deal moving one player to the left. At end of playing time or when each player has had a turn as dealer, scores are counted to determine winner. For more on numerals see numbers 6–12 and 6–35.

NUMERATION – HISTORIC

Activity

2–68. Creativity and numeration might be combined after a study of historical numeration systems (Aztec, Mayan, Egyptian, Chinese, etc.)[15] by suggesting that those pupils who wish try to create a numeration system of their own. Symbols and principles may be original or applied in original ways. (The basic principles of the Hindu-Arabic system are addition, base ten, use of zero, and place value. For the Egyptian system, they were addition, base ten, and repetition.)

Bulletin Boards

2–69. To integrate history and mathematics when studying a social studies unit on Central America, post examples of Aztec and Mayan numeration. Across the top write, "What are Hindu-Arabic equivalents?" Provide scratch pad and pencil. Repeat with Roman, Greek and/or Egyptian, or Chinese numeration.[16]

2–70. To help pupils use historical and modern numerals to record data, let them help find ways in which primitive and mod-

---

[15] *See* Charles F. Howard and Enoch Dumas, *Basic Procedures in Teaching Arithmetic* (Boston: D. C. Heath and Company, 1963), pp. 151–158.

[16] *Ibid.,* see p. 65.

ern humans indicated or recorded number. Make a bulletin board display showing historical progress. On one part of the board daily place a strip of paper with a question such as, "Could Egyptians have recorded the distance from the Earth to the nearest star?" "How would the Mayans have written a numeral for 956?" "How would an astronomer write a numeral for a very large number of miles?" etc. Provide a small pad of paper, a pencil on a string, and an envelope for depositing answers.

History

2–71. Some children may be interested in knowing that the binary system of numeration is said to have been developed by a philosopher named Leibniz (1646–1716) who used one to represent God, and zero to represent the void from which God could create the universe. In a similar way, Leibniz said, man could create any number from one and zero.

Anthropologists report that some primitive peoples have used rudimentary forms of the binary system, probably examples of independent invention.

2–72. Many children will be interested in numeration systems of long ago.[17] Presentation of these may be a separate activity, or it may be combined with an appropriate social studies unit, e.g., the Aztec and Mayan numeration systems may be studied as part of a unit on Central America. In any case, one of the values to be achieved should be a recognition of the mathematical principles employed and how these affected the ease of use and, hence, influenced the progress of mathematics. Especially note the elusiveness of the use of zero, discovered by the Mayans several centuries before it was known to the Hindus. The primitive Aztec numeration system will be seen to be similar to that of the Egyptians. Pupils may wonder that the Greeks achieved greatness in mathematics despite a clumsy system of numerals, but will have little difficulty in understanding the Romans' slow progress encumbered as they were with their numerals to which they and their Latin followers clung all too long.[18]

---

[17] *Ibid.,* see p. 65.

[18] For greater details on historical numeration systems, *see* Florian Cajori, *A History of Mathematical Notations* (La Salle, Illinois: The Open Court Publishing Company, 1928), Vol. I.

a. *Aztec numeration.* Principles employed are repetition, use of a base (20), and addition (in this sense referring to the addition of ones, twenties, four hundreds, etc.—often called the additive principle).

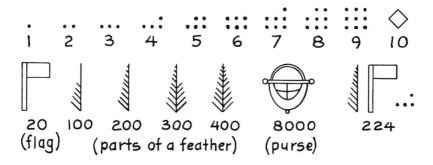

b. *Mayan numeration.* Principles employed are repetition, use of a base (20), use of zero, use of place value, and addition. Except for repetition, these are the same principles as for our familiar Hindu-Arabic system.

Numerals are written upward, the ones' place being at the bottom with a space between it and the twenties. The third place value was 400 for commercial purposes, but was 360 for calendar calculations.

c. *Chinese numeration.* Principles employed are repetition, use of a base (ten), addition (here ones, tens, hundreds, etc.), and multiplication (note that a lesser digit placed to the left of another digit implied that the second was to be multiplied by the first, e.g., $\equiv +$ means 3×10).

d. *Greek numeration.* Principles employed are use of a base (ten), addition, and multiplication (for large numbers only). The first letters of the alphabet represented the first nine natural numbers, the next nine letters represented the tens, and the next nine represented the hundreds.

α	β	γ	δ	ε	ϛ	ζ	η	θ	ι	κ	λ	μ	ν	ξ	ο	π	ϙ	ρ
1	2	3	4	5	6	7	8	9	10	20	30	40	50	60	70	80	90	100

σ	τ	υ	φ	χ	ψ	ω	𝈨	͵α	͵β	͵βφλε
200	300	400	500	600	700	800	900	1000	2000	2535
								(1000×1)	(1000×2)	

e. *Egyptian numeration.* Principles employed are repetition, use of a base (ten), and addition. Note the similarity to the Aztec system.

I	II	III	IIII	III II	III III	IIII III	IIII IIII	III III III	∩	๑	₽
1	2	3	4	5	6	7	8	9	10	100	1000
										(heel bone)	(coil of rope)	(lotus flower)

₽ ๑ ๑ ๑ ∩∩ III
       ∩∩ II
1345

Game

2–73. Roman Bingo. PURPOSE: to provide practice in recognizing Roman numeral equivalents to Hindu-Arabic numerals.

LEVEL: 3 to 6.

NUMBER OF PLAYERS: 2 or more.

MATERIALS NEEDED: A spinner or other device for random selection of one of the following numerals: 1, 2, 3, 4, 5, 6, 7, 8, 9, 10, 14, 19, 40, 50, 55, 60, 90, 100, 105, 500, 1000. A set of bingo-type cards of 16 squares on which appear Roman numeral equivalents to the foregoing Hindu-Arabic numerals; arrange items differently on each card and omit different numerals on each. Beans or other markers.

C	II	IX	M
IV	VI	XIV	III
LX	D	VII	CV
V	XC	I	L

PROCEDURE: Distribute cards and markers. Leader operates spinner and calls out numeral indicated. This he records on paper or chalkboard. Players place markers on Roman numeral equivalent if it is on their cards. The first to get four markers in a row horizontally, vertically, or diagonally calls out "Roman Bingo."
Leader checks to see if he called numerals in the winner's bingo.

NUMERATION – NON-DECIMAL

Activities

2–74. Since electronic computers have become a part of modern life, some children may be interested in computer mathematics. Base two (binary) is used because only two symbols are needed, one and zero; an electric circuit in the machine can be either on (one) or off (zero) or a substance can be magnetized in either of two directions. Hence, for digital computers, numbers are translated from decimal to binary notation. For certain purposes, a less unwieldy notation is useful and since changing between binary and decimal is time consuming, octonal (base eight, generally called octal by computer programmers) is often used.

To translate a binary numeral to octonal, one groups "bits" ("bits" of information, short for "bigits" which is the binary equivalent to "digits") in sets of three beginning at the right.[19]

---

[19] The reason bits are grouped into sets of three is seen when the binary and octonal notations are compared. With only three binary bits one can name numbers zero through seven; with three more bits, one can name numbers through 63; with nine bits, numbers through 511. Note that the next number in each case (8, 64, 512) indicates place value in octonal notation; this is evident from the table below.

Decimal	Octonal	Binary
1	1	1
2	2	10
3	3	11
4	4	100
5	5	101
6	6	110
7	7	111
8	10	1000
.	.	.
.	.	.
.	.	.
64	100	1000000
.	.	.
.	.	.
.	.	.
512	1000	1000000000
.	.	.
.	.	.
.	.	.

If each set of three bits is converted to octonal notation, these sets will name the same number. EXAMPLE: 1001011100_{two} grouped in sets of three is 1 001 011 100; translating each set to base eight we have:

BASE TWO: 1   001   011   100
BASE EIGHT: 1   1   3   4   or 1134_{eight}

The number named in both cases is 604 in decimal notation.

The binary to octonal conversion procedure may be reversed to convert a base eight numeral to one in base two. EXAMPLE: 351_{eight} is 11101001_{two}; 3 becomes 11, 5 becomes 101, and 1 becomes 001 (prefix zeros to make a set of three bits); 351_{eight} names the same number as does 11101001_{two}.

Encourage interested boys and girls to experiment with converting numbers of their own choosing from decimal to binary and octonal. After experimentation and perhaps some research on computers, a committee of pupils might prepare materials for a bulletin board. A parent or other community member who knows about computers might be invited to inspect the bulletin board and to answer children's questions.

Some digital computers are programmed to accept words. To do this, the letters of the alphabet are divided into three groups; each letter in a group is given a number as follows:

	B	A	BA
1	a	j	(skip)
2	b	k	s
3	c	l	t
4	d	m	u
5	e	n	v
6	f	o	w
7	g	p	x
8	h	q	y
9	i	r	z

The word *cat* would be represented as:

c	a	t
B3	B1	BA3.

Converting these symbols to binary notation can be seen from the following:

B	1	1	1
A	0	0	1
8	0	0	0
4	0	0	0
2	1	0	1
1	1	1	1
	c	a	t

Note that B is indicated by 1 in its row, A by 1 in its row, and BA by 1 in each of the B and A rows. Below the representations of B and A, numerals are found for the position of a letter in its group; the binary place values are shown in the left column.

The standard IBM card has bit positions in 12 rows and 80 columns. The rows are numbered from top to bottom in the order 12, 11, 0, 1, 2, 3, 4, 5, 6, 7, 8, 9. In transferring from the accompanying alphabet chart, B is punched in row 12, A in row 11, and BA in row 0 as in the cards illustrated below.

Some children may learn about a part of the process of programming computers through the construction of a chart showing

ABCDEFGHIJKLMNOPQRSTUVWXYZ 0123456789 &2*<-/,.#,$.+_)¢!&>:¦¬'?"=!(

JOSE & EDDIE, CAN YOU FIND MY CAT?

DOMINIC PASCOLI, 1492 MAIN STREET, OLDTOWN, NEW YORK

the representations of all the letters of the alphabet. A part of such a chart is shown below.

	a	*b*	*c*	*d*	...	*p*	...	*z*
B	1	1	1	1		0		1
A	0	0	0	0		1		1
8	0	0	0	0		0		1
4	0	0	0	1		1		0
2	0	1	1	0		1		0
1	1	0	1	0		1		1

With the letters of the alphabet translated for "feeding a computer," children now have a code in which they can write messages for others to decipher.

2–75. Practice on non-decimal numeration may be encouraged if one marks off on ruled paper 11 columns, making the left-hand columns wider than those on the right and numbering them from two to 12. In each column the children should write the numerals from 1 to 12 (or more) in bases to coincide with the numbering of the column, e.g., in column two, write the numerals in the binary system.

2	3	4	5	6	7	8	9	10	11	12
1	1	1	1	1	1	1	1	1	1	1
10	2	2	2	2	2	2	2	2	2	2
11	10	3	3	3	3	3	3	3	3	3
100	11	10	4	4	4	4	4	4	4	4
101	12	11	10	5	5	5	5	5	5	5
110	20	12	11	10	6	6	6	6	6	6
111	21	13	12	11	10	7	7	7	7	7
1000	22	20	13	12	11	10	8	8	8	8
1001	100	21	14	13	12	11	10	9	9	9
1010	101	22	20	14	13	12	11	10	T	T
1011	102	23	21	15	14	13	12	11	10	E
1100	110	30	22	20	15	14	13	12	11	10

2–76. A few pupils may be interested in learning of the advantages claimed for the duodecimal numeration system (base 12).

If so, they should write to the Duodecimal Society of America, 20 Carlton Place, Staten Island, New York, 10304. Qualifying for full membership in the Society requires such skill in the use of duodecimal numeration that it is unlikely that an elementary school child will succeed, but a budding young genius may be found here and there who is both able and interested.

Materials

2–77. To stimulate interest in digital computers, help children make a "machine" to translate numerals from one base to another. Encourage them to invent one, or at least to make suggestions for the construction of one; or, better yet, to invent *and* construct a machine.

One type of numeral translator can be made from a first grade "movie" box. Cover the front with a paper in which three slits are made, one for each notation. On the roller, record numeral equivalents so that as one numeral shows in a slit, the equivalent numerals will show in the other slits.

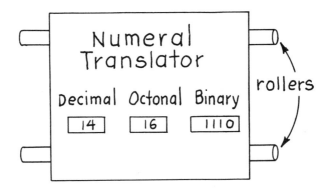

2–78. A device similar to the one described in number 2–77 above can be made to illustrate the "computer language" for the letters of the alphabet (see illustration at the top of page 63). Turn the "machine" so that slits are vertical. The information needed is described on page 59.

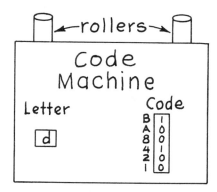

2–79. When practice is needed on finding decimal equivalents to non-decimal numerals, duplicate grids as in the illustration, with only the top line filled in. Give pupils either decimal numerals or binary numerals; they are to supply the equivalents. Similar devices can be made for other bases.

128	64	32	16	8	4	2	1	Decimal Equivalent
			1	0	0	0	1	17
								43
								28
	1	0	1	1	0	0	1	
			1	1	1	0	1	
		1	0	1	1	1	0	

Bulletin board

2–80. To further interest in computer mathematics, prepare a bulletin board announcing some interesting fact, as, "No school on February 22," using the computer code described on page 59.

2–81. To stimulate interest in non-decimal numeration, cut a strip of tagboard for each child. Let each one record his name and birthday, writing all numerals in a base of his own choice. Mount

on a bulletin board with a heading such as "Can You Translate?"
Scratch pad and pencil may be provided if desired.

Games

2–82. Banker. PURPOSE: to provide pleasant practice in using
various non-decimal numeration systems.

LEVEL: 1 to 4.

NUMBER OF PLAYERS: 2 to 4.

MATERIALS NEEDED: A die (singular of dice). A maximum of 20
small squares, 20 strips representing a multiple of the squares
depending on the base se-
lected, ten large squares, **for base 5 use a ▢ for one,**
called "flats," representing
as many strips as the base
indicates, e.g.,

for

a ▭ for five, and a

twenty-five. The strip is five times
the size of the small square while the
large square, or flat, is five times the
size of the strip or 25 times the size of the small square. The
game may be played in any base provided the correct materials
are available.

PROCEDURE: Place the squares, strips, and flats to one side.
Players roll the die in turn. The one getting the largest number
becomes banker. The first player is to the banker's left. He rolls
the die and gets from the banker as many squares as there are
dots on the top surface of the die. If the base for the game is five
and a player accumulates this number of squares, he trades them
in to the banker for a strip. When five strips have been accumulated, they are exchanged for a flat. When play ends, the players
note what number their materials represent. The one with the
largest number wins.

2–83. Nim. PURPOSE: to challenge children of all levels of intel-
lectual ability in an interesting game, and the most capable in an

application of the binary numeration system.

LEVEL: 1 to 6.

NUMBER OF PLAYERS: 2.

MATERIALS NEEDED: A handful of beans or other markers.

PROCEDURE: Place markers in two or more piles, each with a random number of markers. Flip a coin, roll a die, or in some other way decide who shall begin. The first player may remove any number (but at least one) of the markers from one and only one of the piles. His opponent then has the same option. Alternate in this way until one player takes the last marker. He is the winner.

At first children will play without recognizing a pattern by which they can assure victory. Eventually, they may discover that if player A can play in such a way as to leave but two equal piles, he can win. His opponent can only make the piles unequal. Player A can then make them equal again. Continuing in this way, A will take the last marker. For example:

Bill leaves piles	00	00
Joe leaves piles	0	00
Bill leaves piles	0	0
Joe leaves piles	0	
Bill wins.		

When pupils have learned about non-decimal numeration, they should be told that the key to winning lies in the proper use of base two. To win, one should (early in the game) place his opponent at a disadvantage by playing so that if the number of markers in each pile were written in the binary system and the ones totaled, there would be an even number of ones at each place value position, such as the following:

Number in each pile	
Decimal	*Binary*
5	101
3	11
6	110
	222

Note that there are two ones (an even number) in each place

If one can play so as to leave the number of markers in each pile such that, were they enumerated in the binary system, the total of the ones in each place value position is always an even number, he cannot lose.

Music

2–84. To relate music instruction and non-decimal numeration, tell your students that the inhabitants of "Musicland" use a numeration system in which do = 0, re = 1, me = 2, fa = 3, sol = 4, la = 5, ti = 6; then re-do = 7, re-re = 8, re-me = 9, etc. They might make and post a calendar for the month using the numerals of Musiclanders.

ODD AND EVEN NUMBERS

Activity

2–85. As part of a social studies project (or independently) children may make a neighborhood map showing houses and their numbers. Odd-numbered houses will be on one side of a street and even-numbered ones on the other.

Game

2–86. Odd and Even Numbers. PURPOSE: to provide practice in work with odd and even numbers.

LEVEL: 1 to 2.

NUMBER OF PLAYERS: Sets of 2.

MATERIALS NEEDED: Beans or other small markers.

PROCEDURE: Each player takes a number (less than 20) of beans which he holds in a closed hand. His opponent must guess the number. He may ask, "Is it odd or even?" "Is it more or less than _____?" No other clues are permitted. If he guesses the correct amount in three attempts, he scores a point. When the correct answer is given, or after three tries, play goes to the second player. When both have played, the players should change the number of beans.

One of the oldest number games known involved guessing whether the number of small items held in a closed fist was odd or even.

ORDINAL NUMBERS

Materials—see number 2–4.

Game

2–87. Airplane Ride. PURPOSE: to provide practice in using ordinal numbers.

LEVEL: K to 2.

NUMBER OF PLAYERS: 2 or more.

MATERIALS NEEDED: A set of chairs placed as seats in an airliner.

PROCEDURE: Select a hostess who directs passengers to their seats by using ordinal numbers, e.g., "Mr. Smith, your seat is the fourth one." When Mr. Smith is seated, the hostess asks other players, "Did Mr. Smith find the right seat?" If the children answer "Yes," the next passenger is seated. When all seats are filled, the hostess says, "We will now fly to San Francisco." Soon she says, "We are now in San Francisco." As each player leaves the plane, he comments to the hostess on his trip, as, for example, "I enjoyed the view from the fourth seat."

PLACE VALUE AND EXPANDED NOTATION

Activity

2–88. To give pupils practice in various ways of expressing a given numeral, suggest to them that they find how many ways they can rewrite a numeral in "partitioned notation." Choose different numerals for each occasion or for each child. Example: $26 = 20 + 6 = 10 + 16 = 2 + 24 = 18 + 8 = 21 + 5 = \ldots$; or, if desired, maintain the tens by including $30 - 4 = 40 - 14 = 50 - 24 = \ldots$; or $482 = 400 + 80 + 2 = 300 + 180 + 2 = 200 + 280 + 2 = \ldots$

Materials—see number 2–4.

Charts

2–89. When teaching about the principle of place value, use a reading pocket chart. Make cards for the top pocket reading *ones, tens, hundreds.* Pin or tape a piece of dark colored yarn vertically between the pockets for each place. Cut "tickets" from construction paper to use as markers.

With beginners, bundle ten tickets and bind with a rubber band to place in the tens' pocket. Ten bundles of ten tickets can be hung in the hundreds' pocket by placing only part of them in the fold and the balance resting outside. Later one ticket in the tens' place can stand for one bundle of ten tickets. Similarly, a single ticket in the hundreds' pocket will suffice.

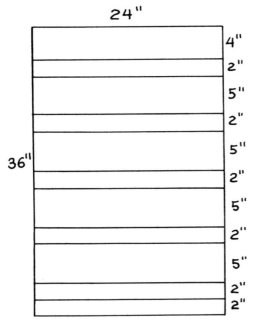

Care should be taken not to give children the impression that a bundle of ten tickets placed in the tens' place of the chart means ten tens. To avoid this possibility, the chart may be used with bundles but without the place value identification cards until time to substitute single tickets for bundles.

2–90. To make a pocket chart for multiple use in mathematics, reading, science, or social studies, you will need lightweight tagboard, heavy cardboard, library tape, and staples. Mark tagboard, as shown in the above illustration and crease to form five pockets.

Staple to the cardboard being sure to hold the pocket creases firmly against the cardboard to reduce sagging while applying two staples to each end of each pocket. Apply tape all around edge.

Games

2–91. Spin a Place. PURPOSE: to provide practice in using the principle of place value.

LEVEL: K to 2.

NUMBER OF PLAYERS: 1 to 4.

MATERIALS NEEDED: A spinner to select numerals 1 to 9. A pocket chart with as many pockets as there are players and with places marked for ones, tens, hundreds. A supply of 1″ x 2½″ construction paper "tickets." Rubber bands.

 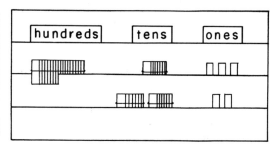

PROCEDURE: Each player spins and places the indicated number of tickets in the "ones'" place of his pocket. On succeeding turns, as a player accumulates ten tickets in his pocket, he secures them with a rubber band and places the bundle in the "tens'" place. After children fully understand that the tens' place indicates the number of sets of ten ones, a single ticket may be used for each bundle of ten tickets from the ones' place. Note: If the bundle is too large, place only part of the tickets in the pocket with the remainder hanging outside.

VARIATION: The same procedure can be followed for work with non-decimal numeration. Merely change the place value cards.

2–92. Expando Relay. PURPOSE: to provide practice in using the principle of expanded notation.

LEVEL: 2 to 4.

NUMBER OF PLAYERS: 2 or more.

MATERIALS NEEDED: Chalk and chalkboard. Cards numbered with those numerals on which expanded notation practice is needed. Two paper bags.

PROCEDURE: Place an equal number of cards in each paper bag. Select teams from among players. (If group is large, make several teams of four to six players each. In such case, a bag of cards for each team is needed.) Designate space on chalkboard for each team and place bag of cards nearby. At signal the first player of each team goes to the bag, pulls out a card, and writes high on the board the numeral and its expanded notation form, e.g., $64 = 6 (10^1) + 4 (10^0)$, depending on kind of practice desired. When finished, he touches the hand of the second player on his team who proceeds as did the first. Continue until all players have had a turn. Note order in which teams finish. Disqualify a team with an incorrect numeral.

S E T S

Activities

2–93. To provide practice in identifying sets of items:

1. Bring a bag containing a variety of familiar objects (spools, cans, blocks, silverware, dolls, etc.). Ask children to sort the objects into sets, first according to criteria you give (short, long, heavy, unpainted, metal, wood, etc.), then according to descriptions they give. Encourage discussions aimed at identifying "well-defined" sets when such an attribute as "heavy" is assigned; children might conclude that one item could be identified as the standard by which other items are judged as "heavier" or "lighter."

2. Let pupils take turns dividing the members of a group into sets by placing each person in a spot designated for those children meeting given criteria. Children should suggest the criteria (sex, color of shoes or other clothing, color of eyes, etc.). Do not overlook the empty set (such as children with lavender polka dot shoes—of which there are probably none).

3. Try to get children to suggest sets of items requiring the use of

senses other than vision (loud and soft sounds, rough and smooth surfaces, sweet and sour foods, etc.).

4. See if children can arrange sets by negative characteristics, e.g., not round, not red, small and not square, not thick and not triangle, etc.

5. Transfer set selection to science and social studies by sorting, according to given criteria, things such as sea shells, seeds, leaves, rocks, people (as by occupations), states, television programs, transportation carriers, or goods (as by ownership).

6. Name a universal set, e.g., children, and ask pupils to name subsets. At first, use concrete materials which can be moved about; later, introduce sets and subsets of items which can be thought about and listed on the chalkboard but not manipulated; e.g., buildings, occupations, or smells.

7. Compare sets by discussing how they are alike and how they are different, e.g., how does the set of boys on the traffic squad compare with the set of teachers in the school?

8. Lead children to discover intersecting sets such as the set of pupils in the band and the set of children who are room monitors.

9. Find the number of various sets and then the number of the union of certain sets. Compare sets by one-to-one correspondence; can one tell which has the largest number without counting the numbers of either set?

Locate sets whose numbers are five, or three, or zero.

10. Consider a set having a given number. Have children close their eyes while the members of the set are separated into two subsets. Is the number the same? Proceed similarly with subsets of varying number, also with more than two subsets.

11. Let children estimate whether one set is equivalent to another set, e.g., are there enough pencils in this box to give one to each pupil? Follow by having children check through one-to-one correspondence. If the sets are not found to be equivalent, which one has more? Less? How many more? How many less?

12. Let children arrange small objects, such as flat beans, into a series of sets such that each is just one more in number than the one before it. Develop the one-more concept of natural numbers.

13. Arrange objects into two sets. Let children determine the number of each and of the total. Then have them close their eyes while the position of the sets is switched. Now check the numbers of the subsets and of the universal set.

2–94. When teaching about the characteristics of sets, use materials such as cutouts of various shapes duplicated in various materials, e.g., diamond shape of thin paper, thick paper, felt, vinyl, wood. Suggest that pupils make sets of similiar shapes or of similar materials.

2–95. When teaching the concept of addition as the union of disjoint sets:

1. Duplicate papers showing a series of two sets containing a variety of numbers of members (pictures or geometric figures). Beside each pair, write N =   . Pupils are to write a numeral indicating the number of the union of each pair of sets.

2. For variation, duplicate papers showing Venn diagrams for non-intersecting sets. Provide pupils with flat beans, corn, or other small objects that will not roll. Write an ordered pair, as (3,4) on the chalkboard. Suggest that children place appropriate numbers of objects in each indicated set and record the number of the union of sets (N = 7).

2–96. When teaching the concept of one-to-one correspondence between the items of one set and those of another, suggest that children see how many items they can think of which represent a one-to-one correspondence; 1 to 2; 1 to 3; 1 to 4.

EXAMPLES:

| 1 to 1 | 1 to 2 | 1 to 3 | 1 to 4 |
| 1 boy, 1 head | 1 boy, 2 hands | 1 yard, 3 feet | 1 car, 4 wheels |

A committee might consolidate lists and display them on the bulletin board.

Materials—see numbers 2–4, 4–24, and 4–25.

SYMBOLISM

Games

2–97. What Relation? PURPOSE: to provide practice on the components of the trichotomy of relations.

LEVEL: 1 to 3.

NUMBER OF PLAYERS: 2 or more.

MATERIALS NEEDED: Chalk and chalkboard.

PROCEDURE: Write on chalkboard:

> $>$ more than
> $=$ equal to
> $<$ less than.

Then write two numerals with a space between them. Call on a pupil to come to write one of the relation signs between the two numerals. If the group agrees that he is correct, let him choose the next player while you write two other numerals.

2–98. Trichotomy of Relations. PURPOSE: to provide practice on the components of the trichotomy of relations.

LEVEL: 2 to 4.

NUMBER OF PLAYERS: 1 or more.

MATERIALS NEEDED: Duplicated papers containing many and varied number patterns depending on proficiency of players.

EXAMPLE:

$(3 \times 1) + 1$	$(2 \times 4) + 3$	$(2 \times 2) \times 2$
$(2 \times 3) + 2$	$(3 \times 2) + 3$	$(3 \times 2) \times 1$
$(4 \times 1) + 3$	$(4 \times 2) + 1$	$(4 \times 1) \times 2$
$(5 \times 2) + 2$	$(2 \times 5) + 3$	$(5 + 3) + 2$

A strip of colored paper with the word *Trichotomy* written on it; pin; Cuisenaire rods[20] or other checking device.

PROCEDURE: Distribute materials to players. Indicate that at a signal they are to write after each pattern the correct relation sign ($<$, $=$, or $>$) between it and the numeral selected by the leader; e.g., if seven is the numeral shown, write < 7 after $(3 \times 1) + 1$. Record names as players finish. The one who has the largest number correct in the least amount of time is the winner and gets to wear the *Trichotomy* crown. Cuisenaire rods may be used as an aid for those who need it or to check if a disagreement arises.

2–99. Symbol Bingo. PURPOSE: to provide practice on mathematical symbols.

---

[20] See number 2–8.

LEVEL: 3 to 6.

NUMBER OF PLAYERS: 2 or more.

MATERIALS NEEDED: Bingo type cards for each player. Arrange symbols in different order on each card. Beans or other markers for each player. A set of flash cards with the definition or an example of each symbol shown on bingo cards. Following are samples:

$\in$	$\emptyset$	$\cup$		is a member of	greater than	intersection
$>$	$\cap$	$<$		Empty Set	Number	Line AB
$\cap$	$\overleftrightarrow{AB}$	$\neq$		Union	less than	not equal to

PROCEDURE: Select a "caller" and distribute cards and markers to players. Caller displays a flash card for a count of five. Each player who recognizes the definition of a symbol on his card covers it with a marker. When a player gets three markers in a row, horizontally or vertically, he calls out "Bingo!" Cards should be checked before writing winner's name on chalkboard.

VOCABULARY

Activities

2–100. To provide practice in the use of terms of comparison, suggest that each child name items that are taller or shorter than himself, heavier or lighter. Make other comparisons according to children's sophistication.

2–101. To provide practice on defining mathematical terms, young children can pretend to explain the meaning over the telephone (i.e., without gestures) to someone who speaks English but does not know the meanings of certain pairs of words, such as, tall-short, near-far, greater than-less than, left-right, up-down, inner region-outer region, and the like.

This is a good activity at parties.

Bulletin board

2–102. To stimulate interest in terms related to geometry, post five to ten squares (not all of the same size) on the bulletin board, each divided by one device or another into a variety of numbers of parts. Number each square. Each day place at the top or bottom of the board a strip of paper on which a question is written, such as, "Which square is largest?", "Which square is divided into most parts?" "Which square is marked off into triangles?" etc. At a corner of the board place a small pad of paper, a pencil on a string, and an envelope. Instructions might be "Write your answer and your name on a paper. Place it in the envelope."

History

2–103. Dictionary. To add interest to mathematical terms and to stimulate the use of reference books, some pupils may want to make a dictionary of definitions and their sources. If the information is written on cards and arranged alphabetically in a file, the project could be cumulative. The following historical facts may be of help to parents and teachers.

> *algebra*—from the Arabic *al-jabr,* meaning reunion of broken parts.
>
> *algorism*—from the Arabic name, al-Khuwarizmi, author of books on arithmetic written in the early ninth century. The Latin translation of these books was known as *algorismus.*
>
> *acre*—from the Anglo-Saxon *aecer,* a furrow long (about ⅛ mile) by a rod wide (as much as a farmer with oxen could plow in a morning).
>
> *area*—from a Latin term meaning a broad piece of level ground.
>
> *arithmetic*—from a Greek word meaning to number.
>
> *baker's dozen*—thirteen, from English bakers' attempts to avoid being accused of short measure.
>
> *barleycorn*—one-third inch, from an early English unit of that name. Shoe sizes are based on barleycorns; the largest size was once 13 (39 barleycorns, 13 inches)—(then each

smaller size was one barleycorn less, each half size was one-half barleycorn less).

carat—from the Arab *carob,* meaning bean.

center—from the Greek *kentron,* a sharp point.

centigrade or *Celsius*—attributed to Anders Celsius, a Swedish astronomer; Fahrenheit minus 32, times five-ninths.

circle—from the Latin *circulus,* a little ring.

counter (as in a store)—from the habit of placing an abacus, or counting frame, on a table where the cost of goods sold was computed.

cubit—the best known of ancient units of length, from the Latin *cubitum,* elbow. The distance from the tip of the elbow to the end of the middle finger.

digit—from a Greek word meaning a finger.

Fahrenheit—from a German physicist named Gabriel Daniel Fahrenheit, nine-fifths times centigrade plus 32.

fathom—the distance between the tips of outstretched hands, six feet.

factor—from a Latin word meaning to make.

foot—the length of the foot from the big toe to the heel.

fraction—from a Latin word meaning to break.

furlong—from two Anglo-Saxon words meaning furrow and long, one-eighth mile.

inch—from the Latin *uncia,* twelfth.

liter—from the Greek *litra,* meaning pound, a metric unit of capacity defined as 1,000 cubic centimeters. A liquid quart is 0.946 liter.

light year—the distance light travels in one year at the rate of 186,000 miles per second or about 6,000,000,000,000 miles.

lug—25 to 30 pounds, considered a reasonable load for a person to lug or carry.

meter—from the Greek *metron* meaning measure, a metric unit of length, once calculated as one ten-millionth of the distance between the equator and the North Pole. It was later changed to the distance (at the temperature of melting ice) between the centers of two marks on a platinum-iridium bar deposited at the International Bureau of Weights and Measures in Paris. The meter is also defined as 1,650,763. 73 times the wave length of orange light from krypton 86. A yard is 0.9144 meter.

mile—from the Latin *mille,* a thousand, a mile is about a thousand paces.

notation—from the Latin *notare,* to mark.

palm—the width of the palm of the hand, four palms equal one foot.

per cent (or *percent*)—from the Latin *per centum,* per hundred.

pound—from the Latin *pondo* meaning pound. The abbreviation, *lb.,* comes from the Latin *libra* also meaning pound.

quart—from the Latin *quartus* meaning fourth.

ratio—from the same Latin root as reason.

rod—from the Anglo-Saxon *rodd,* and derived from the combined length of the feet of 16 men, said to have been measured one Sunday morning after church.

span—from the Anglo-Saxon *spann,* the distance from the tip of the thumb to the tip of the little finger when both are extended, now nine inches.

stone—from the Middle English *ston* used many years ago as a unit of weight but still used by the British, 14 pounds.

sum—from the Latin *summus,* highest.

ton—from the Middle English *tonne,* thought to be the weight of 32 bushels of wheat.

volume—from the Latin *volvere,* to roll.

yard—from the Anglo-Saxon *gyrd,* the length from the end of the nose to the tip of the hand; also thought to be the length of an Anglo-Saxon king's girdle.

zero—an Italian word from the Arabic *sifa,* empty, a cipher.

Games

2–104. Bigger-Smaller. PURPOSE: to provide practice with terms such as "bigger" and "smaller."

LEVEL: K to 2.

NUMBER OF PLAYERS: 1 or more.

MATERIALS NEEDED: Cuisenaire rods.[21]

PROCEDURE: Leader selects a rod, e.g., yellow, and asks players to find how many rods are bigger and how many are smaller.

2–105. What's the Word? PURPOSE: to provide practice on mathematical vocabulary.

---

[21] See number 2–8.

LEVEL: 1 to 4.

NUMBER OF PLAYERS: 2 or more.

MATERIALS NEEDED: Set of word cards or a list of words written on the chalkboard. The vocabulary selected should include items on which practice is needed. First or second grade list might include the following:

1. addition	14. longest	27. spent
2. altogether	15. lower	28. subtract
3. by fives	16. more	29. sum
4. by twos	17. next	30. take away
5. cents	18. nickel	31. taller
6. combination	19. number	32. thicker
7. counting	20. older	33. third
8. each	21. one	34. top
9. first	22. penny	35. upper
10. fourth	23. remainder	36. wider
11. have left	24. second	37. younger
12. heavier	25. shorter	38. zero.
13. less	26. shortest	

PROCEDURE: Divide group into two or three teams; call them Eggheads, Wizards, Geniuses. The teacher or leader selects a word card, holds it up (or gives the number of the word on the chalkboard), and asks the first player on the team of Eggheads to pronounce the word. Then, to show that he knows the meaning, he gives a definition, makes a drawing on the chalkboard, acts out the meaning, or uses some other acceptable procedure. If he succeeds, he scores a point for his team, If he fails, the Wizards may try. The team with most points wins.

2–106. Word Domino. PURPOSE: to provide practice on mathematical vocabulary.

LEVEL: 2 to 5.

NUMBER OF PLAYERS: 2.

MATERIALS NEEDED: 25 or more small cards (1½" x 3") marked with words on which pupils need practice, e.g., number names or names of operations or principles. Make some with the same word at both ends.

thirteen	thirty	associa-tive	identity element	commu-tative	distri-butive
thirteen	addition	closure	seven-teen	multi-plication	inter-section

PROCEDURE: Shuffle cards and deal five to each player. The dealer begins. Play proceeds as in domino. The object is to get rid of cards in one's hand. If one cannot play, he must draw from the deck until he can. At the end of playing time, the one with fewer cards wins (or first to have no cards).

2–107. Word Rummy. PURPOSE: to provide practice on mathematical vocabulary.

LEVEL: 4 to 6.

NUMBERS OF PLAYERS: 2 to 4.

MATERIALS NEEDED: A deck of 52 cards, each with one of the following words on it:

> addition, plus, sum, addend;
> both, two, couple, pair;
> circle, rectangle, triangle, square;
> cup, pint, quart, gallon;
> difference, subtraction, take-away, minus;
> division, divisor, dividend, quotient;
> duet, solo, trio, quartet;
> ones, tens, hundreds, thousands;
> ordinal, first, second, third;
> principle, commutative, associative, distributive;
> second, minute, hour, day;
> set, crowd, bunch, flock;
> yard, feet, inches, mile.

PROCEDURE: Shuffle cards and deal five to each player. Place balance of deck face down on table. Turn up top card. Each player in turn tries to make a book of four related cards. He may take a card from the deck or the turned up one. As he finishes his turn, he discards one card face up. Succeeding players may take all turned up cards or one from the deck. Winner is the one who first has an empty hand.

2–108. Check! PURPOSE: to provide practice on mathematical vocabulary.

LEVEL: 4 to 6.

NUMBER OF PLAYERS: any number.

MATERIALS NEEDED: Paper and pencil, chalk and chalkboard.

PROCEDURE: Teacher or leader is "professor" and writes 20 mathematics terms on the chalkboard, e.g., associative, addend, product, divisor, commutative, equation, etc. Players choose any five terms and write them on their papers. The professor then slowly checks terms at random. As each term is checked, children who had recorded it check it on their papers. The first one to have all of his five terms checked calls, "Check!" He must then come to the chalkboard and explain to the professor the meaning of each term he has checked; if he is successful, he is declared winner; if he is not, the game continues until another player has five terms checked and explained. This is a versatile game and can be used for social studies, science, and spelling words as well as for mathematics.

2–109. Quiz Show. PURPOSE: to provide practice in explaining mathematical terms and procedures.

LEVEL: 5 to 6.

NUMBER OF PLAYERS: 2 or more teams of 5.

MATERIALS NEEDED: List of categories on the chalkboard. These should name topics recently studied, e.g., geometry, problem solving, decimals, measurement. Record at least one category for each team.

PROCEDURE: Divide group into small teams of five players. Give each team a category and five minutes in which to make up five questions about the topic, e.g., Geometry: What is meant by "intersection of lines?" What is a pentagon? What does one call a half-circle? What is a polygon? What is meant by "the face of a polyhedron?" Problem solving: What sequence of activities should be used in solving a story problem? What is an equation? What is meant by "the ratio method?" How does one check to be sure a problem is correctly solved? How does estimating help in problem solving? The captain of the first team selects a category other than his own, and the captain of the team assigned that category asks a question. If the answer is correct, a point is scored. Play then moves to the next team and proceeds as above. At the end of play, the team with the largest score is declared champion.

2–110. Property Tic-Tac-Toe. PURPOSE: to provide practice on the meanings of selected mathematical terms.

LEVEL: 3 to 6.

NUMBER OF PLAYERS: 2 or more.

MATERIALS NEEDED: Pencil and paper. A chart (or chalkboard) listing mathematical properties. A set of cards with each showing a mathematical sentence illustrating one of the properties, as:

PROPERTIES
1. Commutative property of addition.
2. Commutative property of multiplication.
3. Associative property of addition.
4. Associative property of multiplication.
5. Distributive property.
6. Addition property of zero.
7. Multiplicative property of zero.
8. Multiplicative property of one.
9. Multiplicative property of the reciprocal.

$4 + 3 = 3 + 4$
$7 \times 25 = 25 \times 7$
$18 + (23 + 4) =$
$(18 + 23) + 4$
$4 \times (8 + 7) =$
$(4 \times 8) + (4 \times 7)$
$17 + 0 = 17$
$39 \times 0 = 0$
$89 \times 1 = 89$
$3/4 \times 4/3 = 1$

4	9	7
5	3	1
2	6	8

PROCEDURE: Distribute paper and pencil. Place chart where all can see. Direct players to draw a 3 x 3 array of squares and write a numeral from 1 to 9 in each square, in random order. Shuffle cards. Draw one and hold it so all players can see. Each player matches the mathematical sentence with a property shown on the chart; he notes its number and crosses out the corresponding numeral on his paper. Another card is displayed and play continues as before. When a player has crossed out three numerals in a row (vertically, horizontally, or diagonally), he may win if he is the first to call out, "Property!"

The cards may be reshuffled, new arrays drawn by the players, and the game repeated.

2–111. Orange King. PURPOSE: to provide practice on the meanings of selected mathematical terms.

LEVEL: 3 to 6.

NUMBER OF PLAYERS: 2 or more.

MATERIALS NEEDED: Cuisenaire rods.[22] Cards on each of which one of the following is printed: Closure: addition; Closure: multiplication; Commutative: addition; Commutative: multiplication; Associative: addition; Associative: multiplication; Distributive: addition over multiplication; Identity element: addition; Identity element: multiplication.

PROCEDURE: Appoint a leader who arranges cards in random order. When all players are ready, leader selects one card and holds it high, in clear view of all. Players arrange Cuisenaire rods to demonstrate property. The first to finish holds up an orange rod; if his arrangement is agreed to be correct, he lays the orange rod to one side to indicate a point scored. At end of play, the one with most orange rods is declared the "Orange King."

2–112. What's the Unit? PURPOSE: to provide practice on the application of selected measurement terms.

LEVEL: 2 to 6.

NUMBER OF PLAYERS: any number.

MATERIALS NEEDED: Pictures of items (with labels if necessary) which can be measured by procedures which should be known by children. Paper and pencil.

PROCEDURE: Distribute papers. Show a picture and ask each player to record (1) kind of measure, (2) instrument, and (3) unit(s).

---

[22] See number 2–8.

EXAMPLES:

Picture	Responses		
beans	weight	scale	pounds
oil	volume	measuring can	quarts
land	area	surveyor's instruments	acres
floor	area	steel tape	square feet
cloth	length	tape	yards

When completed, check papers to see who has highest score if three points are given for each correct response. Encourage discussion where there is disagreement; you may wish to allow more than a given answer to be correct. For more on vocabulary see numbers 5–28 and 7–28.

Chapter 3

ADDITION AND SUBTRACTION—
WHOLE NUMBERS

FACTS

Activities

3–1. On the chalkboard, draw a picture of a swinging footbridge. On the "bridge" write especially troublesome combinations for certain children. Pupils take turns "crossing the bridge" and back again by naming answers. For those who succeed draw a smiling face at one end of the bridge; for those who fail draw an unhappy face on the rough water below. Emphasize the safe crossings, not the failures.

3–2. Draw on the chalkboard a route of any sort which is of interest to children, for example, the way out of a cave, the path through the woods, or the route to the beach. Write digits along

the "route." Pupils are to "find their way" by adding each number
to the one before it.

Materials

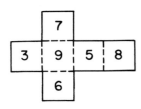

3–3. A motivating device can be had by
making a pair of dice with a digit on
each face. Use wooden cubes or make
from construction paper creased and
taped.

Pupils may roll the dice and add or
multiply the numbers showing on the
top faces.

3–4. Learning addition and/or subtraction facts may be fun by
placing cutouts of several cats, on each of which is a numeral, in
sturdy brown envelopes. Include cutouts of kittens on which there
are number facts also. Children may take an envelope to their
desks or tables and try to match kittens with cats.

Of course cutouts of other animals can be used also.

3–5. To provide practice on troublesome facts, duplicate papers
containing a picture of a pumpkin and eight to ten leaves. On the
pumpkin write a numeral, e.g., 14. Pupils may write on each leaf
an appropriate combination, such as 8 + 6. Pictures may be
varied by using a vase and replicas of the state flower, a Valentine
box and hearts, or other seasonal or local interest items.

3–6. Jigsaw puzzle type cards can be used to
help children learn troublesome facts. Cut each
card differently so that only the correct answer
part will fit.

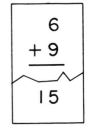

3–7. Practice on facts can be given a "fun" touch
by acquainting pupils with the verse about the old
lady who lived in a shoe and had so many children
she didn't know what to do. Then help boys and
girls make shoe-shaped envelopes large enough to hold a pack

of individual flash cards. As each fact is learned well, its card is placed in the "shoe." Each week pupils count the "children" to see how many now "live in the shoe." (If desired, make flash cards in the shapes of boys and girls.)

3–8. For practice on addition and subtraction facts, help each child make a large paper chart with numerals which represent answers to basic facts to be learned. Pupils may then sort out their individual flash cards by placing them on appropriate numerals.

6	7	8	9	10
11	12	13	14	15
16	17	18	19	20

3–9. To vary practice on facts, make a series of tagboard cards 2″ x 6″. Mark in thirds and crease at the second mark so that the third section may be folded back out of sight. Write in the first spaces an ordered pair and in the third space a numeral to represent the sum of the numbers of the ordered pair. Pupils may be asked to tell what number is related to the ordered pair through the operation of addition. Follow similar procedures for other operations.

3, 5 | 8

crease

3–10. Addition and multiplication facts naming the same number can be assembled and organized for reference or practice by writing the facts on one side of a 3″ x 5″ card and the number represented on the other. Children should make this device for their own use. Sorting the cards is facilitated if a corner is cut from each card.

14

8+6	5+9	
9+5	3+11	11+3
7+7	2+12	12+2
6+8	1+13	13+1
4+10	10+4	

3–11. To provide practice on basic facts, prepare some cards for the pocket chart, each with the picture of a sailor. Make other pieces of "hats" with

slits so they can be set on the heads of sailors. Write number facts on the hats and answers on the sailors.

3–12. Children may enjoy practice on addition and subtraction if one paints a set of eight or ten boxes about the size of a child's shoe box and one round box such as the kind oatmeal comes in. Arrange·to form a "train." Attach a numeral to each car and either leave tops off or make holes. The numerals can represent answers to basic facts, simple problems, or the number of dots or pictures on cards. Pupils deposit problem cards in cars showing appropriate numerals.

3–13. For individual practice on basic facts a particular child finds difficult, make several folders by creasing 5″ x 7″ cards so that, folded, they will be 2½″ x 7″; staple near the crease of each. Write facts which are difficult for a certain child to learn on the top, or cover, page; write answers on the under sheet.

$$\frac{\begin{array}{ccccc} 4 & 5 & 8 & 7 & 6 \\ +7 & +6 & +5 & +8 & +5 \end{array}}{}$$

3–14. To add interest to the teaching of basic facts, bore 20 ¼″ holes at one inch intervals along a 1″ x 2″ board. Use brightly colored pegs to show addition and subtraction facts, e.g., six red pegs and five blue ones show that $6 + 5 = 11$.

3–15. Learning addition and subtraction facts at home or at school can be stimulated if, using heavy construction paper, one makes several sets of two disks, one smaller than the other. On the smaller disk, write basic facts on one side with answers on the other side—back to back. Cut a window in the larger circle in a way such as to show one basic fact at a time. Use a paper fastener to hold the circles together.

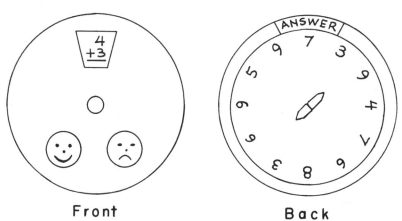

Front   **Back**

3–16. Practice on troublesome basic facts can be secured by changing the board for the common ring toss game (see Sum Throw, number 3–111). Use a face such as a Jack-O-Lantern, Santa Claus, Easter Bunny, or a geometric shape. Score one for each correct answer.

3–17. For practice on his own troublesome basic facts, help a child make a "learning machine." Fold a

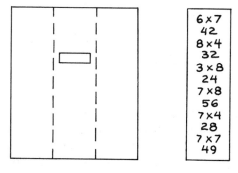

9″ x 12″ sheet of construction paper in thirds to make an open-ended envelope 3″ x 12″. Cut an opening 2¼″ x ½″ about three

| 6×7 |
| 42 |
| 8×4 |
| 32 |
| 3×8 |
| 24 |
| 7×8 |
| 56 |
| 7×4 |
| 28 |
| 7×7 |
| 49 |

or four inches from one end. Next provide a strip of tagboard 2½″ x 12″ (or longer). On the strip the pupil may write, alternately at half-inch intervals, a fact followed by the answer. When the strip is slipped into the envelope, a fact will show through the window and when the strip is pulled, the answer will show for checking.

3–18. To give practice on troublesome basic facts, construct a "house" from a box so that two windows will show basic facts and a door may be opened to show the answer. If the facts are written on paper attached to rollers, the items can be changed quickly.

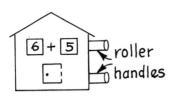

A roller "movie" box can be used also by placing a piece of cardboard to cover the answer.

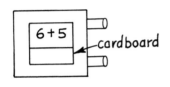

3–19. Troublesome basic facts can be displayed for practice on a three dimensional figure made by cutting two hexagons of the same size from construction paper. Crease lightly along radii. Lay one on the other with creases outward and tape the edges. Cut out one triangle, pull the several edges together, and tape.

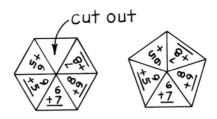

3–20. A device for individual study of basic facts can be had by making a fat fish with a wheel on the back so that one addend or factor is constant and is written on the mouth, one shows through the eye opening, and the correct answer (on the wheel) is under a fin. Pupils may practice giving answers to facts. When in doubt, they can check by looking under the fin.

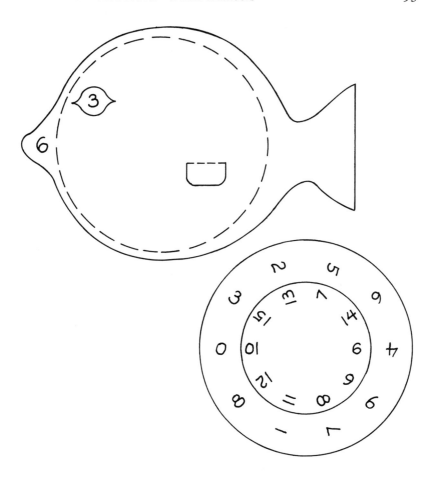

3–21. To demonstrate the relative values of numbers and combinations of numbers, make a simple balancing scale by bending a common wire clothes hanger so as to lower the fulcrum. Tape a clothespin to each end. A paper cup may be attached to each clothespin (or taped directly to each end of the hanger). Cuisenaire rods[1] or similar materials can be weighed to show that combi-

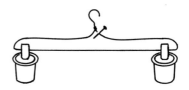

---

[1] See number 2–8.

nations of certain kinds will balance, e.g., two light green and one light red will balance one brown. A similar scale can be made from a piece of wire twisted into a loop at the center and turned up a half inch at each end. Attach a string to the center loop, or hang the device on a nail. Attach cups or clothespins to the turned-up part.

3–22. For practice on addition and/or subtraction, prepare a device of tagboard on which equations are indicated, showing only some numerals or operation signs. Make slits where items are missing and prepare tagboard cards marked with numerals or operation signs. Pupils insert cards in appropriate slits.

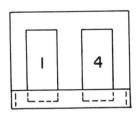

$$\underline{\quad} + \underline{\quad} - 3 = 9$$
$$8 - \underline{\quad} + 5 = 10$$
$$6 \underline{\quad} 5 - 4 = 7$$

3–23. For displaying answers to oral problems, a single-pocket chart holder is useful. Help children make their own by folding an inch of a 6″ x 6″ piece of construction paper. Staple the pocket ends. Cards 2½″ x 4″ can be used for displaying answers.

3–24. To provide practice in computation or on basic facts, display on a pocket chart a series of problems on cards placed vertically to the left. Place answer cards at random on the right. Pupils must place correct answer in the pocket containing the problem.

3–25. To help individualize the learning of arithmetic, purchase two copies of each of a number of workbooks. Record answers for every page on a slip of paper which is then pasted or taped to the back of the sheet. Since there are two of each page, both sides can be used. Label according to topic and order to be used, e.g., "Division using two-digit divisors, fourth." File in a box or drawer available to children. Pupils may work on scratch paper and check their own work; if a clear plastic envelope is available, the work may be done with a grease pencil on the plastic and then erased with a piece of cleansing tissue.

3–26. Many children are fascinated by an electric board with a colored light which illuminates when metal bolt heads representing a fact (or problem) and an answer are touched by each of two wires. It has many uses in addition to arithmetic, e.g., matching any kind of question with its answer, pictures of objects and their names, words and definitions, names of capital cities and of states or nations.

Change wiring now and then to prevent children from making correct responses merely from knowing the location of points which will make the light glow.

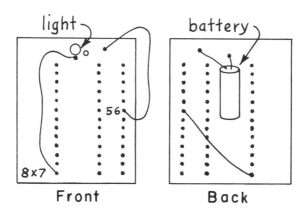

A sample of the wiring diagram for one item is illustrated. When one end of a wire is touched to the bolt beside *8 × 7* and the other wire is touched to the bolt beside *56*, the light will show.

For other materials which can be adapted for use in teaching addition and subtraction facts, see number 2–4.

Bulletin boards

3–27. To stimulate the learning of addition and subtraction facts, place cutouts of seasonal items, e.g., pumpkins for autumn, on

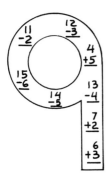

the bulletin board. As each child demonstrates his knowledge of a set of basic facts, print his name on one of the pictures.

3–28. To keep troublesome addition and subtraction facts before children, cut large (24″ to 30″ tall) numerals from colored paper; on them write basic facts, the answers to which are the number represented. Mount on the bulletin board. Change numerals each week.

Mobile

3–29. To keep arithmetic facts or other items before children, enlist their help in cutting out colored cardboard or plastic geometric figures. On each print a troublesome fact or word. Suspend these by nylon thread from slim pieces of reed (or plastic drinking straw or wire) of different lengths. Each pair should balance but not with the fulcrum at midpoint. Balance the lowest one first. Hang from the ceiling.

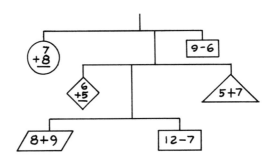

History

3–30. Scratch Addition (to show how addition computations were done many years ago). Four hundred years ago a popular method of performing addition was the scratch method in which computations were made from left to right.

```
              1 6            1 6 5              7
  478        4̸78            4̸7̸8             1̸65
  924        9̸24            9̸2̸4             4̸7̸8
 +365       +3̸65           +3̸6̸5            9̸2̸4
          _____     _____        +3̸6̸5
           3+9+4=16        6+2+7=15        _____
                                            6+1=7
```

```
     7             7 6
    1̸1            1̸1̸
  1̸657          1̸6̸57 ⎫
  4̸7̸8̸          4̸7̸8̸  ⎬ ◄──    the sum
  9̸2̸4̸          9̸2̸4̸  ⎭        is 1767
 +3̸6̸5̸         +3̸6̸5̸
 _____     _____
  5+4+8=17        5+1=6
```

Games

3–31. Bean Guess. PURPOSE: to provide practice in subtraction facts.

LEVEL: K to 2.

NUMBER OF PLAYERS: 2 or more.

MATERIALS NEEDED: A supply of beans.

PROCEDURE: Divide group into teams of two. Distribute a given number of beans to players, e.g., ten. One member of each pair places his hands behind him and divides the beans so that some are in each hand. Keeping one fist closed, he opens the other for his opponent to see and so to tell (or guess) how many are in the closed hand. If he is correct, he gets one of the beans (otherwise none) and then has his turn as above. His opponent should note that the total in this case is one more than when play began. After play has proceeded so that there has been some shifting of beans from one to another, beans should be counted before each turn. At the end of play, children count to see who has the most beans.

3–32. Equal. PURPOSE: to provide practice in addition facts.

LEVEL: 1 to 2.

NUMBER OF PLAYERS: 4 or more.

MATERIALS NEEDED: Numerals (on cards) for addends on which the players need practice.

PROCEDURE: Distribute one card to each player with instructions to stand in a circle and hold the card right side up in front where all can see. Say, "Five and Three, where is your equal?" Children holding five and three go to Eight and say, "Here is our equal; five plus three equals eight." Equals stand together. After a time, players should exchange cards. For subtraction, say "Six minus four; who is your equal now?" Child holding six goes to stand beside Two and says, "Here is my equal; six minus four equals two."

3–33. Circle Addition. PURPOSE: to provide practice in addition facts.

LEVEL: 1 to 2.

NUMBER OF PLAYERS: 4 to 10.

MATERIALS NEEDED: Colored cardboard circles numbered from 0 to 9.

PROCEDURE: Players stand in a ring, each holding a numeral circle. First player says, "I am seven. Who can make me 11?" The player who has the numeral four says, "I am four. I'll make you 11." Play proceeds around the ring. Players must try to "make" only those numbers possible using numbers indicated by the cards of other players.

3–34. Patterns. PURPOSE: to provide practice in addition facts.

LEVEL: 1 to 2.

NUMBER OF PLAYERS: 1 or more.

MATERIALS NEEDED: Cuisenaire rods.[2] Paper and pencil.

PROCEDURE: Distribute materials to each player. Explain that when the leader writes a numeral on the chalkboard (or holds up a card on which the numeral is written), each player is to write down all the combinations of numbers which add up to equal the number indicated. If the game is new to any of the players, illustrate what is meant, e.g., if the numeral is 5, players are expected to record $3 + 2$, $2 + 3$, $4 + 1$, $1 + 4$, $(2 + 2) + 1$, $(1 + 1) + (1 + 2)$, etc. The first one to finish is to raise his

[2] See number 2–8.

hand. Record names in the order of hands raised. When most of the players have finished, check the combinations given by the one who finished first. If all his are correct, check to see who has found more. The winner is the first one who recorded the most correct combinations. Cuisenaire rods may be used as an aid for those who need it and to check combinations challenged by any player.

3–35. Fact Rummy. PURPOSE: to provide practice in addition facts.

LEVEL: 1 to 2.

NUMBER OF PLAYERS: 2 to 4.

MATERIALS NEEDED: A set of 90 cards, two each of the addition facts with sums of ten or less.

Sums of 10 or less

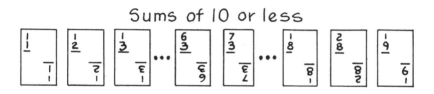

PROCEDURE: Shuffle cards and deal five to each player. Lay balance of cards in a pile face down; turn up top card. Player to left of dealer begins by laying down "books" of three or more cards containing facts with the same sum, e.g., $\frac{3}{2}$, $\frac{4}{1}$, $\frac{1}{4}$. He may draw one card from the blind deck or take the turned up card. If he (on this turn or a later one) finds another fact having the same sum, he may add it to his book. When through playing, he discards one card face up. Play then goes to his left and continues as above except that should there be more than one card in the discard pile; a player may take one, part, or all of them (he must take from top down, e.g., he cannot choose the second card down without also taking the top one). Play ends when one person has no more cards. Player with most cards in his books wins.

3–36. Rod Facts. PURPOSE: to provide practice in addition facts.

LEVEL: 1 to 3.

NUMBER OF PLAYERS: 2 to 4.

MATERIALS NEEDED: Cuisenaire rods,[3] paper, pencil.

PROCEDURE: Place Cuisenaire rods at center of table around which players sit. Leader selects a rod and gives it a number, e.g., six. Each player makes as many combinations as he can and records them on his paper. Pupil with most correct combinations wins and play is repeated with winner as leader. At the end of the game, children count total of all combinations; the one with the largest number is declared the master winner.

An alternate way of scoring might be to ask each player to report his discoveries to the leader who makes a master list. The number of combinations for each rod is recorded and a total found. The group findings could be recorded on the chalkboard or the bulletin board.

3–37. Odd or Even? PURPOSE: to provide practice in addition or multiplication facts.

LEVEL: 1 to 3.

NUMBER OF PLAYERS: 2.

MATERIALS NEEDED: A deck of 40 cards each marked with a numeral from 0 to 9. An addition or multiplication table.

PROCEDURE: Shuffle cards and divide into two piles to be placed face up in front of the players. The first player names the sum of the first two cards and states whether it is odd or even. If he is correct, he may keep the cards; if not, the cards are placed in a pile to one side. Play then goes to the next player. In case of disagreement, the players refer to a table. When all cards in the two piles are used, the discard pile is shuffled and divided into two piles and play continues. At the end of the game, the player with most cards is declared winner. (May be played also for practice on multiplication facts.)

3–38. Subtraction Cards. PURPOSE: to provide practice in subtraction facts.

LEVEL: 1 to 2.

NUMBER OF PLAYERS: 2.

MATERIALS NEEDED: Two sets of cards, each with numerals 0 to 18, one numeral per card.

---

[3] See number 2–8.

PROCEDURE: Shuffle cards and divide them between the players placing each stack face down. Each player turns up a card. The pupil whose card shows the larger number must give difference. This will be his score. Continue until play time is gone or until cards are all turned up. Pupils may need help in computing final scores. (An alternate scoring procedure is to give one point for each correct answer.)

3–39. Relatives. PURPOSE: to provide practice in subtraction facts.

LEVEL: 1 to 3.

NUMBER OF PLAYERS: 3 or more.

MATERIALS NEEDED: Subtraction flash cards. A set of cards, numbered 0 to 9.

PROCEDURE: Players form a semicircle. Distribute a flash card to each. The first player holds up a flash card and selects another player to get the answer card from the number cards displayed in the chalk tray or on a table. The player then asks, "Who are my relatives?" All children who have "relative" cards hold up their flash cards.

player   relatives

| 7-4 | | 3 | | 9-6 | | 4-1 | | 8-5 | | 5-2 | etc.

3–40. Snap. PURPOSE: to provide practice in addition and/or subtraction facts.

LEVEL: 1 to 2.

NUMBER OF PLAYERS: 1 or more.

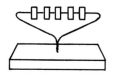

MATERIALS NEEDED: For each player make a device of wood block, wire coat hanger, and plastic spring clothespins. Cut hook from coat hanger and insert neck into hole drilled in wood block (or suspend in usual way).

PROCEDURE: Teacher or leader says, "I am thinking of a number that is two plus three." Children arrange clothespins to show the answer.

3–41. Family Train. PURPOSE: to provide practice in addition and/or subtraction facts.

LEVEL: 1 to 2.

NUMBER OF PLAYERS: 2 to 10.

MATERIALS NEEDED: Chalk and chalkboard.

PROCEDURE: Divide children into two groups. The first player in each group goes to the chalkboard and drawns a train engine; on it he writes a numeral, an engine number designated by the teacher or a leader, e.g., 8. The second player then comes up to draw a coach on which he writes a combination making the number shown on the engine, e.g., 6 + 2. Continue until a member of the group thinks all combinations have been shown; he then draws a caboose. The team whose train shows all combinations for the engine number wins.

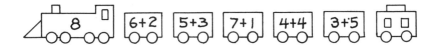

3–42. Add a Tail. PURPOSE: to provide practice in addition and/or subtraction facts.

LEVEL: 1 to 2.

NUMBER OF PLAYERS: 2 or more.

MATERIALS NEEDED: Flash cards, chalkboard, and chalk.

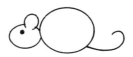

PROCEDURE: Divide group into two or more teams. Present a flash card to the first member of each team. The first to answer correctly wins the round. For him draw part of a simple picture of a rat. Continue in this manner until the drawing of one rat is completed (draw the tail last). The team first getting a tail drawn is the winner.

3–43. Combination Draw. PURPOSE: to provide practice in addition and/or subtraction facts.

LEVEL: 1 to 2.

NUMBER OF PLAYERS: 2 to 6.

MATERIALS NEEDED: A deck of flash cards containing the addition and subtraction combinations on which the players need practice.

PROCEDURE: Place cards face down at the center of the table. Each player, in turn, draws a card and gives the answer to the combination on it. If he is correct, he may keep the card; if not, he places it face up on the table. The next player may give the answer to the face up card, keep it, and draw a card. If there is more than one card face up, the player who can give the answer to each may keep it as well as draw from the deck. At the end of play, the one with most cards is declared winner.

3–44. Going to the City. PURPOSE: to provide practice in addition and/or subtraction facts.

LEVEL: 1 to 2.

NUMBER OF PLAYERS: 3 to 10.

MATERIALS NEEDED: Flash cards of combinations on which the players need practice. Chairs.

PROCEDURE: Arrange chairs to form a "train." Each child goes to the teacher's desk for a "ticket" (flash card) and then takes a seat on the train. A child who is selected to be conductor collects the tickets; as each is collected, the passenger must tell the answer. If he cannot, he must take his ticket home and wait for the next train.

3–45. Where Is My Family? PURPOSE: to provide practice in addition and/or subtraction facts.

LEVEL: 1 to 2.

NUMBER OF PLAYERS: Group or class.

MATERIALS NEEDED: A card with a number fact on it for each child. Select according to need for practice, e.g., $3 + 1$, $2 + 2$, $1 + 3$, $4 + 0$, $0 + 4$. Subtraction facts may be included if desired.

PROCEDURE: Distribute cards, one to a player. Select one child to come to stand at the front of the room. He holds his card for all to see and says, "Where is my family?" All children who have cards showing number facts, related to that of the child at the front, parade before him. If he agrees that they are indeed members of his "family," he introduces them by reading their "names" as they hold up their cards for all to see. The family then looks about the room to see if any relatives failed to come up. Another player is selected and the foregoing procedure repeated.

3–46. Honor Roll. PURPOSE: to provide practice in addition and/or subtraction facts.

LEVEL: 1 to 3.

NUMBER OF PLAYERS: 2 or more.

MATERIALS NEEDED: Flash cards; for each player, a set of 3″ x 5″ cards with answers to flash card facts to be practiced; card holders for each player. Make card holders of colored poster paper, 9″ x 6″. Fold 1½″ and staple to form a pocket.

PROCEDURE: All players begin with a score of ten. Teacher or leader holds up a flash card. Each player selects an answer from among his cards and places it in his card holder. If he selects the wrong answer, he loses a point; he should record missed facts for later study. At the end of play, all those with intact scores of ten get their names written on the chalkboard in colored chalk.

3–47. Trimming the Christmas Tree. PURPOSE: to provide practice in addition and/or subtraction facts.

LEVEL: 1 to 3.

NUMBER OF PLAYERS: 3 or more.

MATERIALS NEEDED: A Christmas tree which may be real or drawn on the chalkboard. Fancy cards with questions or combinations on them; each should have a string loop attached for fastening to the tree or a bit of masking tape if a chalkboard tree is used.

PROCEDURE: Place cards face down. Each player in turn takes a card and, if he can give the correct answer (or sum, difference, quotient, or product), he may place it on the tree; if he cannot give the answer, the card is placed under others.

VARIATION: Write combinations on papers shaped like pumpkin seeds, placing these in a pumpkin (real or artificial). Children take turns reaching into the container and pulling out a "seed." If they can give the answers to the facts shown, they may keep the seeds; otherwise they must return them to the pumpkin. Pupils may record combinations they do not know for "pumpkin seed homework."

The above game can be adapted further to fit in with individual, local, or seasonal interests, such as hearts in a Valentine box, eggs in an Easter basket, rabbits in a pen, cars in a used car lot, or animals in a barnyard.

3–48. Matching. PURPOSE: to provide practice in addition and/or subtraction facts.

LEVEL: 1 to 3.

NUMBER OF PLAYERS: 4 or more.

MATERIALS NEEDED: Depending on the time of the year, make paper pumpkins, apples, Christmas cards, Valentines, Easter eggs, or the like. Cut each in two in an irregular manner. On one part write an arithmetic combination and on the second part write the answer. Use whatever facts the children need to practice.

PROCEDURE: Divide group into two parts and distribute parts containing combinations to half the players and parts on which are answers to the other half. Each player must find who has a part to match his own. When all players have found partners, ask each one who has a combination to say what it is and his partner to give the answer. Redistribute materials and repeat.

VARIATION: For one or two players, place all materials on a table and let children find matching parts.

3–49. Barrel of Facts. PURPOSE: to provide practice in addition and/or subtraction facts.

LEVEL: 1 to 3.

NUMBER OF PLAYERS: 1 or more.

MATERIALS NEEDED: An outline of a barrel on the chalkboard.

PROCEDURE: Write a numeral at the top of the barrel. Players take turns writing facts, the answer to which is the selected number. If competition is desired, draw outlines of two barrels and have teams see which can record most facts to "fill the barrel."

3–50. Tight Rope. PURPOSE: to provide practice in addition and/or subtraction facts.

LEVEL: 1 to 3.

NUMBER OF PLAYERS: 1 or more.

MATERIALS NEEDED: Chalk and chalkboard.

PROCEDURE: With chalk, preferably colored, draw a picture of a tightrope. Write numerals over the rope and another numeral on the picture of an umbrella which the "acrobat" will use to help him keep his balance. Each player tries to "walk the tight-rope" by adding the number represented on the umbrella to those indicated on the tightrope, or by multiplying the umbrella number by the numbers on the rope. By substituting appropriate numerals on the tightrope, practice may be had in subtraction or division.

3–51. Mystery. PURPOSE: to provide practice on addition and/or subtraction facts and on solving equations.

MATERIALS NEEDED: Paper and pencil, equation cards such as $\boxed{5 + \square = 9}$, bag of old costume jewelry, as many police badges as players (dime store variety or paper replicas).

PROCEDURE: Distribute paper and pencil. Explain game carefully, since once started, game should not be interrupted. Tell a "mystery" story such as: "Once there was a rich traveller whose jewels were taken from his hotel room. The police were notified and they found 12 clues leading to the missing jewels. (As he tells the story, the teacher places 12 equation cards about the room in full view of all the pupils.) I am the chief of police and I deputize each of you as policemen to help find the missing jewels. Are you ready? Then, help me find the jewels." Players write names on papers and proceed to solve the 12 equations. As each finishes, he brings his paper to the teacher; if it is correct, the teacher pins a badge on him. The one who has the neatest paper gets to have the bag of jewels on his desk until recess.

3–52. Octopus. PURPOSE: to provide practice in addition and/or subtraction facts.

LEVEL: 1 to 3.

NUMBER OF PLAYERS: 1 or more.

MATERIALS NEEDED: A drawing, on chalkboard or tagboard, of an octopus. On each tentacle, write a numeral from 2 to 9, inclusive.

PROCEDURE: Write a numeral on the body of the octopus. Each player is to try to "keep the octopus in his cave" by adding or multiplying the number represented on the body and one of the numbers indicated on the tentacles.

By substituting appropriate numerals, practice can be had in subtraction and division.

3–53. Our House. PURPOSE: to provide practice in addition and/or subtraction facts.

LEVEL: 1 to 3.

NUMBER OF PLAYERS: 1 or more.

MATERIALS NEEDED: Chalk and chalkboard.

PROCEDURE: Draw a picture of a house on the chalkboard. Ask a child if he can show all the "relatives" of four plus three. He writes the addition and subtraction combinations on the house to show who lives there. If he is correct, he may choose the next player.

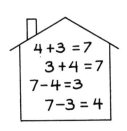

Multiplication and division related facts may be substituted for addition and subtraction.

3–54. Family Fun. PURPOSE: to provide practice in addition and/or subtraction facts.

LEVEL: 1 to 3.

NUMBER OF PLAYERS: 1 or more.

MATERIALS NEEDED: Chalk and chalkboard.

PROCEDURE: Draw a picture of a house and yard. Write a numeral, e.g., 8, on the house. Say, "On a warm sunny day, all

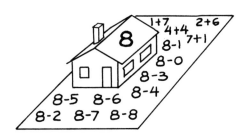

the family of eight were in the yard enjoying the sunshine. Who can show me their names?" Call on a volunteer to write the basic facts "in the yard." Ask other players if any members of the family are still indoors. When all are accounted for, erase the facts, write a different numeral on the house, and proceed as before. Basic facts may be written either vertically or horizontally, e.g.,   3 or 3 + 5.
       +5

3–55. Falling Through the Ice. PURPOSE: to provide practice in addition and/or subtraction facts.

LEVEL: 1 to 3.

NUMBER OF PLAYERS: 2 or more.

MATERIALS NEEDED: Flash cards of arithmetic facts.

PROCEDURE: Players sit in semicircle "around the frozen lake." Leader shows flash cards and calls on individuals at random. Anyone who fails to answer correctly "falls through the ice." He may get out again if he can answer correctly after someone else has fallen in.

3–56. Save the Women and Children. PURPOSE: to provide practice in addition and/or subtraction facts.

LEVEL: 1 to 3.

NUMBER OF PLAYERS: 1 or more.

MATERIALS NEEDED: A cardboard "boat" with slots for flash cards. (Select those on which children need most practice.)

PROCEDURE: Players take turns trying to see how many women and children they can save from the sinking boat by giving the answers to combinations as they take flash cards from the boat.

3–57. Circus Balloons. PURPOSE: to provide practice in addition and/or subtraction facts.

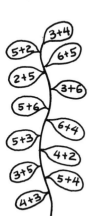

LEVEL: 1 to 3.

NUMBER OF PLAYERS: 1 or more.

MATERIALS NEEDED: Pictures of balloons on the chalkboard. Write a combination on each.

PROCEDURE: Players take turns trying to "pop the balloons" by giving answers to combinations. Leader or children may clap hands to indicate the pop of the balloon.

VARIATIONS: Similar games can be played by varying the pictures, e.g., show a flower garden with combinations on each flower; players will "pick the flowers."

3–58. Jack and the Beanstalk. PURPOSE: to provide practice in addition and/or subtraction facts.

LEVEL: 1 to 3.

NUMBER OF PLAYERS: 1 or more.

MATERIALS NEEDED: Picture of a beanstalk with combinations written on the leaves.

PROCEDURE: Players pretend to be Jack and try to "climb the beanstalk" by naming the answers to combinations.

3–59. Fact Board. PURPOSE: to provide practice in addition and/or subtraction facts.

LEVEL: 1 to 3.

NUMBER OF PLAYERS: 2.

MATERIALS NEEDED: A cardboard playing board marked with 45 squares (nine rows of five squares each); in each square write a combination. A set of 60 squares of cardboard slightly smaller than the squares on the playing board; on 45 write the answers to combinations on the board and on 15 write other numerals.

PROCEDURE: Turn all squares face down. Players take turns turning up a square and finding its place on the board. If a player cannot find a place for his square, either because it does not belong or because he does not realize that it *does* belong, he loses his turn and must place the square before him. When all squares have been turned up, the winner is the one who has the fewest in the pile before him.

3–60. Fact Relay. PURPOSE: to provide practice in addition and/or subtraction facts.

LEVEL: 1 to 4.

NUMBER OF PLAYERS: 4 or more.

MATERIALS NEEDED: Duplicated papers containing as many rows of arithmetic facts as there are players on each team. Select facts on which children need practice: addition, subtraction, multiplication, or division.

PROCEDURE: Divide group into two or more teams with team members sitting near each other. Distribute paper face down to first players on each team. At a signal the first players turn paper over and write answers to first row of facts. Then pass papers to second players who do second row, and so on. Check answers and record number correct on each paper. Team finishing first gets an additional ten points, second place gets eight points, third place gets six points, and fourth place gets four points.

3–61. Shooting Gallery. PURPOSE: to provide practice in addition facts.

LEVEL: 1 to 4.

NUMBER OF PLAYERS: 2 or more.

MATERIALS NEEDED: A large chart or flannel board on which are arranged ten pictures of targets such as at a county fair side-show. Beside, or on, each target is a numeral from zero to nine (use random order).

PROCEDURE: Players try to hit the targets by adding a given number to each number shown on the targets.

The game may be varied by requiring products or by changing the numerals to show dividends or minuends; division or subtraction could be required.

3–62. Wolf and Sheep. PURPOSE: to provide practice in addition and/or subtraction facts.

LEVEL: 1 to 4.

NUMBER OF PLAYERS: 3 or more.

MATERIALS NEEDED: None.

PROCEDURE: Players are sheep and form a circle with one person in the center who is the wolf. He calls a sheep by name and gives a combination. The sheep must answer correctly or join the wolf. In the latter case, he may get back to the circle by giving the answer to the next combination before the sheep called on can do so or by giving the correct answer if a wrong one was accepted by the wolf.

VARIATION: The wolf may ask a question to be answered by the sheep or name a term which must be explained or defined by the sheep.

3–63. Postman. PURPOSE: to provide practice in addition and/or subtraction facts.

LEVEL: 1 to 3.

NUMBER OF PLAYERS: 1 to 4.

MATERIALS NEEDED: Postoffice mail boxes. Instead of names, write numerals for sums, differences, products, or quotients. "Letters" have combinations.

PROCEDURE: Players take turns "sorting the mail" by placing the "letters" in the correct boxes.

Vary the game by having any type of matching desired.

3–64. Who Are You? PURPOSE: to provide practice in addition and/or subtraction facts.

LEVEL: 1 to 4.

NUMBER OF PLAYERS: 2 to 19.

MATERIALS NEEDED: 3″ x 5″ cards with numerals from zero to eighteen written on them.

PROCEDURE: Pin one or more cards on each player. Leader says, "Who is nine plus five?" Player who has 14 says, "I am 14." Leader continues with addition and subtraction facts for which players have sums or differences.

VARIATION: Substitute multiplication or division facts and give players appropriate answer cards.

3–65. Equation Line-up. PURPOSE: to provide practice in arithmetic facts and in relations between numbers.

LEVEL: 1 to 4.

NUMBER OF PLAYERS: 10 or more.

MATERIALS NEEDED: Two sets of number cards, 0 to 9, for each player. One each of cards with such operation, relation, and variable signs as required for the practice desired:

$$+ - \times \div > < = \square \,.$$

PROCEDURE: Choose five children to come to the front of the room to hold up cards to form an open sentence, e.g., $4 + \square = 9$. Pupils at seats hold up the answers from their number cards. After five equations have been shown, select five other children to come to the front of the room.

3–66. Traveling. PURPOSE: to provide practice in addition and/or subtraction facts.

LEVEL: 1 to 4.

NUMBER OF PLAYERS: 4 or more.

MATERIALS NEEDED: Flash cards of combinations which need practice. (Game can be played orally with no materials.)

PROCEDURE: One child is selected to "take a trip." He begins by standing beside a seated child. Both look at flash card and try to be first to give answer. If the seated player wins, he exchanges places with the traveler and stands beside the next player. The object is to see who can travel the farthest.

3–67. Pull the Sled up the Hill. PURPOSE: to provide practice in addition and/or subtraction facts.

LEVEL: 1 to 4.

NUMBER OF PLAYERS: 1 or more.

MATERIALS NEEDED: Drawing of hill on chart or chalkboard. Write numerals 1 to 9 in random order on slope. On picture of sled write a numeral.

PROCEDURE: Players take turns "pulling the sled up the hill" by giving sums of the number represented on the sled and those on the slope. Change sled number as needed. Products may be given,

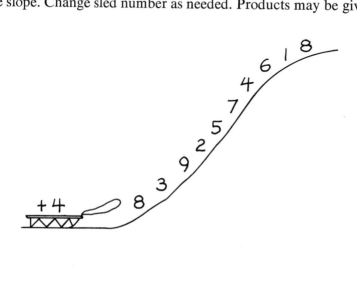

or by writing minuends or dividends on slope, pupils may give differences and quotients.

3–68. Do You Know Me? PURPOSE: to provide practice in addition and/or multiplication facts.

LEVEL: 1 to 4.

NUMBER OF PLAYERS: 2 or more.

MATERIALS NEEDED: A large card with a numeral on it. Pin. Small cards with other numerals.

PROCEDURE: Pin the large card on one child who is known as Stranger. Distribute small cards to other players who keep them out of sight. Stranger asks another, "Do you know me?" The second answers by giving the sum (or product) of his number and that of Stranger, who must then say, "Oh, then you must be _____." When all have been identified, choose another Stranger and have other players exchange cards.

3–69. Circle of Facts. PURPOSE: to provide practice in addition and/or subtraction facts.

LEVEL: 2 to 3.

NUMBER OF PLAYERS: 5 or more.

MATERIALS NEEDED: Cards numbered from 0 to 9, one for each player.

PROCEDURE: Players form a circle and hold number cards in full view. The teacher or leader may begin the game by saying, "Carla, add your number to Lee's," or "Tony, subtract your number from Sue's."

3–70. More. PURPOSE: to provide practice in addition and/or subtraction facts.

LEVEL: 2 to 4.

NUMBER OF PLAYERS: 2 to 4.

MATERIALS NEEDED: Four or five sets of cards numbered 0 to 9.

PROCEDURE: Shuffle cards and place them face down at the center of the table. Players decide operation—addition, multiplication, or subtraction—to be used. Each player, in turn, draws two cards and gives the sum, product, or difference of the numbers represented, according to agreed operation. If a player miscalculates, his cards are put back on the bottom of the pile. At the end of each round, the player whose answer is the largest number collects the cards of the other players. The player with most cards at the end of play is the winner.

3–71. What Number Am I? PURPOSE: to provide practice in addition and/or subtraction facts.

LEVEL: 2 to 4.

NUMBER OF PLAYERS: 2 or more.

MATERIALS NEEDED: None.

PROCEDURE: The teacher or leader describes a number by using addition and subtraction, e.g., "If you take me away from eight, I leave three, or if you add me to three, I make eight." The player naming the correct answer then becomes leader.

3–72. Nickname. PURPOSE: to provide practice in addition and/or subtraction facts.

LEVEL: 2 to 4.

NUMBER OF PLAYERS: 2 to 10.

MATERIALS NEEDED: None.

PROCEDURE: One child who is "It" selects a number from 1 to 20 and tells it to the group; he also thinks of a fact for which his number is the answer. Other players try to guess what "nickname" the child had in mind; they may give addition or subtraction facts, e.g.,"Is it seven plus four?" The child who correctly guesses the nickname then becomes "It," and play proceeds.

This game may be adapted to work with multiplication and division facts.

3–73. Combination Relay. PURPOSE: to provide practice on addition or subtraction facts, and on adding a seen number to an unseen number—mental computational skill.

LEVEL: 2 to 4.

NUMBER OF PLAYERS: Two teams.

MATERIALS NEEDED: Two sets of number cards from 1 to 9 (or as needed for practice).

PROCEDURE: Select two teams and distribute number cards so that opposite players have the same number. Designate a score-keeper. When the teacher or leader calls a number, the first player on each team adds it to the number on his card (or each may subtract, multiply, or divide the two numbers). The one who first gives his correct answer gets a point. After each player has had a turn (or when time for this activity is up) calculate team scores by totaling points earned.

3–74. Eraser Hat. PURPOSE: to provide practice in addition and/or subtraction facts.

LEVEL: 2 to 4.

NUMBER OF PLAYERS: 2 or 3 teams.

MATERIALS NEEDED: Chalkboard eraser for each team, chalk, chalkboards.

PROCEDURE: Divide group or class into two or three teams. The first player on each team goes to the front chalkboard and places an eraser on his head. The teacher or leader calls a number at which players hurry to back of room being careful not to lose the eraser balanced on the head. A second number is called as pupils near the rear of the room. If there is a rear chalkboard, the children write down both numerals; otherwise they touch the back wall and hurry to the starting place where they write the sum of or difference between the two numbers. The first player with the correct answer gets a point. When all players have had a turn, the scores are calculated by counting points.

3–75. Rocket to the Moon. PURPOSE: to provide practice in addition and/or subtraction facts.

LEVEL: 2 to 4.

NUMBER OF PLAYERS: 2 to 6.

MATERIALS NEEDED: Flash cards. Flannel board with cut outs of the moon and of two rockets.

PROCEDURE: The teacher or leader shows a flash card to the first player on one team. If he answers correctly, his team's rocket advances one space toward the moon. Play alternates from one team to the other.

3–76. Magic Number. PURPOSE: to provide practice in addition and/or multiplication facts.

LEVEL: 2 to 5.

NUMBER OF PLAYERS: 2 to 6.

MATERIALS NEEDED: Forty playing cards—four sets of cards each with a numeral 0 to 9 on it.

PROCEDURE: Dealer announces whether the game shall be addition or multiplication and what the "magic number" will be (for addition any number from 0 to 18, for multiplication any product of two numbers 0 to 9). Deal all cards face down. The first player turns up one of his cards. The next does the same. This continues until one player recognizes that two of the exposed cards yield the sum or product agreed upon; he must say "magic number" before anyone else does. He may then collect all exposed cards, after which play continues as before. Should a player call "magic number" at the wrong time, he must give each player one of his cards. Play ends when one player is without cards. The winner is the one with most cards.

VARIATION: Limit picking up to the pair of cards which show the numbers yielding the magic sum or product.

3–77. Show a Number. PURPOSE: to provide practice in addition facts.

LEVEL: 3 to 4.

NUMBER OF PLAYERS: 2 to 6.

MATERIALS NEEDED: Two sets of cards, each with a numeral from 0 to 9, for each player.

PROCEDURE: The dealer announces, "Make 17 (or any other number less than 19)," then deals five cards to each player, and arranges the next ten cards in this pattern:

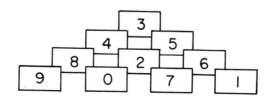

Beginning at the dealer's left, each player in turn lays down in front of him all the combinations he can make of any two numbers equalling the number called. He may use the cards in his hand and any cards, from the pattern on the table, that have two or more exposed corners (as 3, 9, 0, 7, 1 in the above illustration). When all players have had a turn, scores are recorded by giving one point for each combination showing. The game ends when each player has been the dealer once. Highest total score wins.

3–78. Spin a Sum. PURPOSE: to provide practice in addition facts.

LEVEL: 3 to 4.

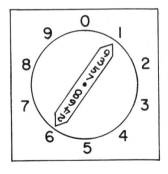

NUMBER OF PLAYERS: 1 to 10.

MATERIALS NEEDED: Dial and spinner.

PROCEDURE: Players take turns flipping the spinner. Orally each adds the number pointed to on the dial to each of the numbers on the ends of the spinner, as in diagram: 1 + 9, 1 + 3, 1 + 5, 1 + 7; 6 + 2, 6 + 4, 6 + 6, 6 + 8. One point is scored for each player who makes no mistakes.

3–79. Equations. PURPOSE: to provide practice in addition and subtraction facts.

LEVEL: 2 to 6.

NUMBER OF PLAYERS: 2 to 6.

MATERIALS NEEDED: 50 cards, on each of which one digit appears—five each of digits 0 to 9. Six cards with equal signs, six with plus signs, and six with minus signs.

PROCEDURE: Place equal, plus, and minus sign cards in middle of table, face up. Deal three digit cards to each player; place balance of cards face down in center of table. Play begins to the dealer's left. Each player, in turn, draws a digit card and tries to make an equation, selecting signs as needed, such as $5 + 2 = 4 + 3$ or $2 + 3 = 7 - 2$. If he cannot do so, he discards one card face up, and play goes to next player, who may draw from blind deck or take the card that is face up. When one person makes an equation, he is declared winner and game begins again with a different dealer.

Multiplication and division signs may be substituted for plus and minus or all four used.

For other games which can be adapted to provide practice in addition and subtraction facts, see numbers 4–2, 4–4, 4–6 through 4–9, 4–12, 4–35, and 4–39.

Verses

Verses help motivate the learning of certain addition and subtraction facts through rhymes.

3–80. One plus one equals two,
One for me and one for you.
Two plus two equals four;
If you like this, let's do some more.
Four plus four equals eight,
It's not hard to get that straight.
Five plus five equals ten.
Now let's do it all again.[4]

3–81. One minus one equals nought,
Never is found but often sought.
Two minus one equals one,
Isn't this the greatest fun?
Three minus one equals two,
There's another we can do.
Four minus one equals three,
See how easy it can be.[5]

---

[4] Mary Reed, *Counting Rhymes* (New York: Simon and Schuster, 1946), p. 20.
[5] *Ibid.*, p. 21.

COMPUTATIONS

Activities

3–82. Assign pupils several equations and suggest that they draw sketches to illustrate possible steps of the solution. Do not expect all children to solve a given problem in the same way. Example:

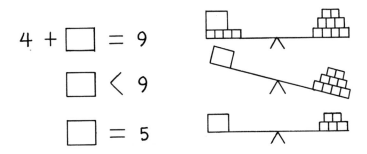

3–83. A helpful activity to assist children in grasping the social uses of subtraction is to discuss with them examples of situations in which each type is used. With their help, list many for each. Examples:

Type 1.	Finding what part of a group is left.	Joe had 28¢ and spent 12¢. How much did he have left?
Type 2.	Comparing two groups.	Tom had 18 marbles. Jim had 14. Tom had how much more than Jim?
Type 3.	Finding how many more are needed.	Ann had 18¢. How much more would she need to buy a pen costing 25¢?
Type 4.	Finding an unknown number when the sum and one addend are known.	Sue has 27 stamps. 16 are foreign. How many stamps are domestic?

Social uses of subtraction and other operations can be illustrated also through role playing using real or play money and equipment. Pretend to operate a gas station, a yardage store, or a grocery store. At times, use Cuisenaire rods[6] in place of money. Perhaps some children need to make an inventory following a day's business to find how much merchandise is *left*. Other pupils may need to keep records of each day's business. Children may suggest other necessary activities.

3–84. To provide practice in solving equations, duplicate a series of equations that are related such that a given geometric figure represents the same number wherever it is found. Different shapes represent different numbers. The pupil must solve equations in sequence. Example:

$$\square + 5 = 9$$
$$(2 \times \square) + (3 \times \triangle) = 17$$
$$(\triangle + \square) - (\triangle - 2) = 3$$
$$(\square + \triangle) + (\triangle - \square) = (\triangle \times \triangle) - (\triangle + 1)$$

3–85. For children who get bored with arithmetic but who still need practice on basic facts, suggest some "front end" adding and multiplying.

Addition	Multiplication
4682	967
7349	× 87
+ 6754	72
17	48
16	56
17	63
15	42
18,785	49
	84,129

3–86. Pupils can get much practice in computation by pretending to order items that interest them from a mail order catalog. They should fill out the order blank including total cost, tax, shipping weight, and shipping charge.

---

[6] See number 2–8.

3–87. When studying the commutative principle, children may enjoy thinking of sequences of activities which are reasonably commutative and others which are not. Examples: Putting on shoes and then putting on a sweater can be commutative with putting on a sweater and then putting on shoes. But putting on socks and then putting on shoes cannot be commutative with putting on shoes and then putting on socks.

3–88. As children listen to or sing "The Twelve Days of Christmas," suggest that they assume one gift will be given each day beginning with December 25. Then on what date will the donor run out of partridges? (Since 12 partridges were given, the last would be sent on January 5.) Follow with 22 turtle doves. And so on. Will there be enough gifts to last a whole year?

3–89. Here are procedures for constructing magic squares which may be of interest to some pupils (see also numbers 3–99 and 4–20).

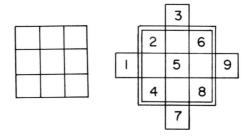

a. For a 3 by 3 magic square, first make a grid. Then add a square, or cell, on each side. Now number the cells in a diagonal pattern as shown in the illustration. It will be seen that some cells are blank. Fill these by moving the numerals in the outside cells to empty cells as far removed as possible but in the same column or row, eg., move 1 to the cell between 5 and 9. Pupils should experiment to see if the numbering of cells could begin with some number other than 1, e.g., 6, 7, 8 . . . , or instead of proceeding by 1's, if the numbering could be by 2's, 5's, or some other consistent order.

2	7	6
9	5	1
4	3	8

b. To make a 16 cell magic square, fill a grid of 16 cells with the numerals from one to 16 in the usual sequence. Note that the sum of the diagonals is 34. Therefore all rows and columns must also total 34. This can be accomplished in either of two ways.

1	2	3	4
5	6	7	8
9	10	11	12
13	14	15	16

1	15	14	4
12	6	7	9
8	10	11	5
13	3	2	16

Leave the numerals in the four corners and the four numerals at the center but exchange positions of the others at the greatest distance possible, e.g., 2 and 15 change places.

Another procedure is to leave in position those moved in Figure B. Instead, the corner numerals are exchanged diagonally and the positions of the four center numerals are exchanged, also diagonally.

16	2	3	13
5	11	10	8
9	7	6	12
4	14	15	1

3	4	5	6
7	8	9	10
11	12	13	14
15	16	17	18

c. Make a 16-cell grid and number from the upper left corner as shown. Begin with any number of your choice. Next exchange the opposite corner numerals, i.e., 3 and 18, 6 and 15; then do the same with the four inner numerals, i.e., 8 and 13, 9 and 12. Do you now have a magic square? Could you have started numbering at any other point in the grid, i.e., at the upper right cell, and proceeded downward?

d. The numbers shown on the diagonal of the illustration add to 30. So should the other diagonal, as well as each row and column. Find the missing numbers. (Top row: 12, 7; middle row: 6, 14; bottom row: 13, 8.)

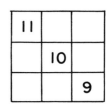

3–90. Magic circles also are fun. The three numbers on each straight line will be found to have the same sum. Pupils might like to try making other simple magic circles of this sort.

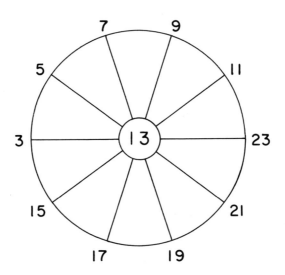

3–91. Increase mathematics learning by taking advantage of activities which might be studied as part of another curricular area.[7] Consider items such as:

Constructing and operating a store
Making a mural
Cooking or baking
Sewing
Planning a party
Taking an excursion
Making gifts
Arranging a bulletin board

Publishing a class newspaper
Measuring play space for games
Keeping graphs and records of progress
Planning and carrying out a science experiment or demonstration
Preparing for a puppet show
Making a monthly calendar
Raising money for welfare

3–92. Interesting practice in addition can be had from developing a Fibonacci series. In such a series, each number after the first

---

[7] For social studies suggestions, *see* Enoch Dumas, *Arithmetic Learning Activities* (Palo Alto, California: Fearon Publishers, 1957).

two is the sum of the two preceding numbers, e.g., 3, 2, 5, 7, 12, 19, 31, 50, 81, 131, . . .

After explaining how one constructs a Fibonacci series, ask a pupil to write on the chalkboard, while your back is turned, such a series of ten numbers, choosing for himself the two numbers with which he will begin. When he has finished, turn around, glance at his numbers, and then write the sum of his series. You can do this quickly because the sum of the Fibonacci numbers in a series of ten is 11 times the seventh number. In the series above, the seventh number is 31. ($11 \times 31 = 341$.) You can compute this easily by beginning $10 \times 31 = 310$, then $310 + 31 = 341$.

So that pupils get practice in addition as they try to find the trick you used, ask each one to write a Fibonacci series on his paper. You will move about the room giving the sum of his series. He should check your answer. Note that the sum is ($55 \times$ the first number) $+$ ($88 \times$ the second number) or $11[(5 \times$ the first number) $+$ ($8 \times$ the second number)]. In the example above, $11[(5 \times 3) + (8 \times 2)] = 341$. Note the progression below.

$$
\begin{aligned}
3 &= a \\
2 &= b \\
5 &= a + b \text{ or } 3 + 2 \\
7 &= a + 2b \text{ or } 3 + 4 \\
12 &= 2a + 3b \text{ or } 6 + 6 \\
19 &= 3a + 5b \text{ or } 9 + 10 \\
31 &= 5a + 8b \text{ or } 15 + 16 \\
50 &= 8a + 13b \text{ or } 24 + 26 \\
81 &= 13a + 21b \text{ or } 39 + 42 \\
131 &= 21a + 34b \text{ or } 63 + 68 \\
\hline
341 &= 55a + 88b \text{ or } 165 + 176
\end{aligned}
$$

3–93. Palindromic Numbers. Many children may be motivated to practice addition by starting with any number and adding to it the number obtained by reversing the digits. In many cases the sum will read the same from either end, e.g., $142 + 241 = 383$. If it does not, the digits of this sum may be reversed and added to the sum; the process should be repeated until a sum is reached which can be read the same from either end (said to be palindromic).

Children should record the number of steps needed and classify the numbers with which they work as one-step, two-step, three-step, etc. For example, 142 is a one-step number; 149 is a two-step number (149 + 941 = 1090, 1090 + 901 = 1991); 158 is a three-step number (158 + 851 = 1009, 1009 + 9001 = 10010, 10010 + 1001 = 11011).

Classified below are many of the numbers less than 1000 which require three or more additions before a palindromic "sum" is reached. Note that often several numbers have the same "sum." Since some numbers require a large number of steps (89 requires 24 steps), they are not listed. Selecting from the numbers listed, practice exercises can be provided to fit the abilities and needs of particular children. For example, one might ask pupils to find the palindromic sums and the number of steps needed to reach them for the following numbers: 257, 185, 69, 280, and 97.

3 steps

"Sum"	Numbers
11,011	158, 257, 356, 455, 554, 653, 752, 851, 950
13,431	168, 267, 366, 465, 564, 663, 762, 861, 960
15,851	178, 277, 376, 475, 574, 673, 772, 871, 970
3,113	199, 298, 397, 496, 694, 793, 892, 991
5,115	249, 348, 447, 546, 645, 744, 843, 942
5,335	299, 398, 497, 596, 695, 794, 893, 992
6,666	156, 255, 354, 453, 552, 651, 750
8,888	157, 256, 355, 553, 652, 751, 850
6,996	186, 285, 384, 483, 582, 681, 780
7,337	349, 448, 547, 745, 844, 943
7,117	389, 488, 587, 785, 884, 983
7,557	399, 498, 597, 795, 894, 993
9,119	439, 538, 637, 736, 835, 934
9,559	449, 548, 647, 746, 845, 944
9,339	489, 588, 687, 786, 885, 984
9,779	499, 598, 697, 796, 895, 994
4,444	155, 254, 452, 551, 650
2,662	164, 263, 362, 461, 560
4,884	165, 264, 462, 561, 660
2,552	184, 283, 382, 481, 580
4,774	185, 284, 482, 581, 680
2,992	194, 293, 392, 491, 590
1,111	59, 68, 86, 95
747	180

4 steps

5,115	174, 273, 372, 471, 570
9,559	175, 274, 472, 571, 670
9,339	195, 294, 492, 591, 690

4,884	69, 78, 87, 96
25,652	539, 638, 836, 935
23,232	579, 678, 876, 975
22,022	599, 698, 896, 995
45,254	629, 728, 827, 926
44,044	649, 748, 847, 946
47,674	679, 778, 877, 976
46,464	699, 798, 897, 996
13,431	183, 381, 480
6,996	192, 291, 390
69,696	729, 927
68,486	749, 947
67,276	769, 967
66,066	789, 987
89,298	819, 918
88,088	839, 938
2,662	280
2,552	290

5 steps

79,497	198, 297, 396, 495, 594, 693, 792, 891, 990
45,254	166, 265, 364, 463, 562, 661, 760
44,044	176, 275, 374, 473, 572, 671, 770
59,895	549, 648, 846, 945
99,099	639, 738, 837, 936

6 steps

45,254	182, 281, 380
44,044	79, 97
475,574	779, 977
449,944	799, 997
881,188	889, 988

7 steps

233,332	188, 287, 386, 485, 584, 683, 782, 881, 980
881,188	197, 296, 395, 593, 692, 791, 890
45,254	190

8 steps

1,136,311	589, 688, 886, 985
233,332	193, 391, 490

10 steps

88,555,588	829, 928

Materials

3–94. A variation of the pocket chart (see number 2–89) which is useful in teaching carrying and borrowing is made by fastening three transparent plastic boxes to a board. Label the one on the right "Ones," the next "Tens," and the last, "Hundreds." Two-inch pieces of ⅛″ doweling make convenient markers for accumulating and bundling with a rubber band, or exchanging ten in one box for one in the next box to the left to illustrate carrying. The process can be reversed in the case of borrowing.

3–95. Two rulers may be used as a device for adding numbers, e.g., to add 4 and 3, find 4 on one ruler and place the zero point of the second ruler there; then find 3 on the second ruler; it will be opposite 7 on the first ruler.

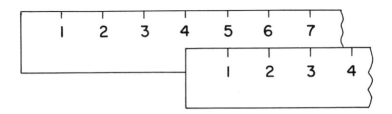

Of course, in both examples above, the inverse operation of subtraction also can be shown. One reads the devices differently, just as one reads an addition table differently to find subtraction answers. The rulers shown above indicate that $7 - 3 = 4$ just as they show that $4 + 3 = 7$.

3–96. On a 30″ x 1″ x 1″ board, mark off points at two-inch intervals. Mark the center zero and number in each direction. Place cup hooks at each mark. Balance carefully. Use heavy

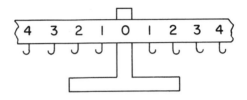

washers of equal weight or clothespins to show equations such as $4 + 3 = 7, 5 + 2 = 3 + 4, 6 + 2 = 4 + 2 + 2$.

Charts

See numbers 2–89 and 2–90.

Bulletin boards

3–97. To stimulate interest in computations, post correct and incorrect examples of addition and subtraction problems. Number each. Make a heading reading, "Which ones are correct?" Provide paper, pencil, and a deposit envelope.

3–98. To follow up a discussion of number properties, prepare ‚a bulletin board entitled, "Properties of Whole Numbers," and show these as:

Commutative

$$N\{\triangle\triangle\triangle\triangle\} + N\{\triangle\triangle\} = N\left\{\begin{matrix}\triangle\triangle\triangle\\\triangle\triangle\triangle\end{matrix}\right\} = N\{\triangle\triangle\} + N\{\triangle\triangle\triangle\triangle\}$$

Associative

$$\left(N\{\triangle\triangle\} + N\{\triangle\triangle\triangle\}\right) + N\{\triangle\triangle\triangle\triangle\} = N\left\{\begin{matrix}\triangle\triangle\triangle\\\triangle\triangle\triangle\\\triangle\triangle\triangle\end{matrix}\right\} = N\{\triangle\triangle\} +$$
$$\left(N\{\triangle\triangle\triangle\} + N\{\triangle\triangle\triangle\triangle\}\right)$$

Distributive

$$N\{\triangle\triangle\triangle\triangle\} \times \left(N\{\triangle\triangle\} + N\{\triangle\triangle\triangle\}\right) = N\left\{\begin{matrix}\triangle\triangle\triangle\triangle\triangle\\\triangle\triangle\triangle\triangle\triangle\\\triangle\triangle\triangle\triangle\triangle\\\triangle\triangle\triangle\triangle\triangle\end{matrix}\right\} = \left(N\right.$$
$$\left.\{\triangle\triangle\triangle\triangle\} \times N\{\triangle\triangle\}\right) + \left(N\{\triangle\triangle\triangle\triangle\} \times N\{\triangle\triangle\triangle\}\right)$$

or as:

Commutative

$$4 + 2 = 6 = 2 + 4$$

Associative

$$(2 + 3) + 4 = 9 = 2 + (3 + 4)$$

Distributive

$$4 \times (2 + 3) = 20 = (4 \times 2) + (4 \times 3)$$

History

3–99. Magic Square. The oldest known magic square[8] is said to have been found by Emperor Yu of China carved on the back of a tortoise shell about 4000 years ago.[9] It is known as the *lo-shu*.

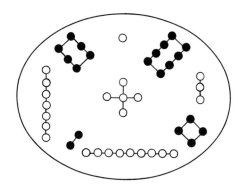

6	I	8
7	5	3
2	9	4

The *lo-shu* looked some-what like this.

We would show it this way.

---

[8] For other magic squares, *see* numbers 3–89, 3–116, 4–20, 6–15, and 6–16.

[9] David Eugene Smith, *History of Mathematics* (New York: Dover Publications, Inc., 1953), p. 591, Vol. II.

3–100. Pascal Triangle. The Pascal Triangle was known to Chinese mathematicians through the writing of Chu Shï-kié in 1303. It appeared in this form:

```
                  1
              1       1
          1       2       1
      1       3       3       1
  1       4       6       4       1
1       5      10      10       5       1
                 etc.
```

Pascal explored its properties in 1654, and, since then, it has carried his name. Note that (1) each number except the one at the top is the sum of the numbers just above it to the left and the right, e.g., $2 = 1 + 1$ and $3 = 1 + 2$; (2) each number, except 1, is the sum of all the numbers in the diagonal beginning with the number just above it to the left or the right, e.g., $10 = 4 + 3 + 2 + 1$ and $10 = 6 + 3 + 1$; (3) each diagonal shows an arithmetic sequence, e.g., 1, 2, 3, 4, . . . or 1, 3, 6, 10, . . . , and from this, one can predict what the next number in each sequence will be if he can determine the nature of the sequence, as:

					arithmetic sequence
1,	1,	1,	1,	1, ...	zero order
1,	2,	3,	4,	5, ...	first order
1,	3,	6,	10,	15, ...	second order
1,	4,	10,	20,	35, ...	third order
1,	5,	15,	35,	70, ...	fourth order
		etc.			

Another predictive pattern is found by adding the numbers shown in each row of the triangle.

1	$= 1$	Each succeeding number in the
$1 + 1$	$= 2$	totals column is twice the one
$1 + 2 + 1$	$= 4$	before it. The total of the num-
$1 + 3 + 3 + 1$	$= 8$	bers in the next row will be
$1 + 4 + 6 + 4 + 1$	$= 16$	16×2 or 32.

The Pascal Triangle can be used in the classroom to give practice in adding and in exploring relationships. After exhausting the possibilities when the triangle is started with one (called the generator): (1) begin with two or some other number; check to see if the properties discovered when one was the generator still hold; (2) then use a sequence for the sides and again check properties; (3) follow with random numbers along the sides.

(1)
```
            2
        2       2
    2       4       2
2       6       6       2
            etc.
```

(2)
```
                2
            3       3
        4       6       4
    5       10      10      5
                etc.
```

(3)
```
            4
        2       2
    1       4       1
7       5       5       7
            etc.
```

Fractions can be used as generators to provide practice for middle grade pupils.

```
                ½                                    ⅛
            ½       ½                            ¼       ¼
        ½       1       ½                    ½       ½       ½
    ½       1½      1½      ½            1       1       1       1
½       2       3       2       ½ 2      2       2       2       2
            etc.                                    etc.
```

Games

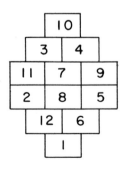

3–101. Equation Hop Scotch. PURPOSE: to speed up mental addition.

LEVEL: 2 to 5.

NUMBER OF PLAYERS: Two teams of 1 to 5 pupils each.

MATERIALS NEEDED: Hop scotch design on floor or playground (may be made on wrapping paper and taped to floor using masking tape).

PROCEDURE: First player on one team hops on squares of his choice, calling out the numbers as he lands on them and inserting signs to make an equation, e.g., "One plus 12 minus five equals eight." If he does this correctly, his team gets one score. Play alternates between teams.

3–102. Secret Operations. PURPOSE: to provide practice in work with equations, and in mental arithmetic—keeping in mind one operation while experimenting with a second.

LEVEL: 2 to 4.

NUMBER OF PLAYERS: 2 or more.

MATERIALS NEEDED: Duplicate on papers a number of equations involving two or more operations with the operation signs omitted, e.g., $(7 \bigcirc 4) \bigcirc 5 = 8$ for $(7 - 4) + 5 = 8$; $(9 \bigcirc 2) \bigcirc 8 = 10$ for $(9 \times 2) - 8 = 10$.

PROCEDURE: At a signal players try to "break the code" by inserting correct signs. As each finishes, he stands. Record names in order of completion. Check to see if each is correct. Indicate first, second, and third places after disqualifying those with errors.

3–103. Mathmountains. PURPOSE: to provide practice in mental arithmetic.

LEVEL: 2 to 4.

NUMBER OF PLAYERS: 2 teams of 4 players each.

MATERIALS NEEDED: Chalkboard or pencil and paper.

PROCEDURE: On the board or on a sheet of paper write three columns of numerals with 15 numerals in each column in the range 1 to 25 and centering around 8, with repetitions allowed, the greatest number of these being in the 6 to 10 range. A sample listing is shown at the right.

The two teams may be named Southians and Northians living on opposite sides of the "Mathmountains," represented by the 3 by 15 array of numerals.

Southia		Northia
3	11	9
17	8	5
5	13	2
12	1	7
6	9	18
3	12	9
4	0	7
2	15	13
7	8	9
12	16	3
1	15	0
7	3	11
15	6	9
3	2	12
9	8	6

Starting with the first member of the Southians, and alternating between teams, each team member tries to successfully cross the "Mathmountains." This is done by threading out a path of three numbers, one from each column, whose sum is 25. (Numbers and sum can be altered to suit class and level.) As a player succeeds in crossing he marks his route and thus makes those numbers inaccessible to following players (see sample route marked in the diagram). The team that succeeds in getting the greater number of its members across is declared winner.

3–104. Bean Bag Toss. PURPOSE: to provide practice in addition.

LEVEL: 2 to 5.

NUMBER OF PLAYERS: 2 or more.

MATERIALS NEEDED: Two bean bags. Concentric circles on the floor or playground with two barrier marks an appropriate distance from opposite sides of the circles—four feet for second graders, six or eight feet for fifth graders. Number the circles according to the ability of the players.

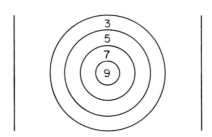

PROCEDURE: Divide group into two teams, each to line up on opposite sides of the circles behind the barrier marks. Select a scorekeeper. First player of one team tosses his bean bag as near the center of the target as he can. He scores points according to values indicated; if the bag stops on a dividing circle, he scores the larger number. The first player on the second team then tosses his bean bag. Players then retrieve bags and let second players throw. As each player finishes (except the first), he goes to the scoreboard and adds his score to the one before and thus provides his team's accumulated score. For third and fourth graders, values of strikes may be greater than ten. For fifth and sixth graders, fractions and mixed numerals might be assigned.

3–105. Beat the Time. PURPOSE: to provide practice in addition and subtraction and in mental arithmetic—keeping in mind an unseen number to which a seen number is added.

LEVEL: 2 to 4.

NUMBER OF PLAYERS: 1 or more.

MATERIALS NEEDED: Duplicated papers showing numerals 1 to 100 in random order and with space for writing another numeral under each one shown. A sandglass or kitchen timer. A set of cards for each player on which directions are given such as: Add 4, Add 7, or Subtract 6.

PROCEDURE: Distribute papers. Leader (or one player) draws a card and shows it to all players. He then sets the timer for a given number of minutes, three to ten, and places it in full view. All players proceed to follow the direction given, e.g., add four to each number shown on their papers, to see how many computations can be done in the time allotted. If the same direction is followed for a second attempt, pupils can work against their own scores.

3–106. Add a Circle. PURPOSE: to provide practice in addition.

LEVEL: 2 to 5.

NUMBER OF PLAYERS: 3.

MATERIALS NEEDED: Paper, pencil, compass. On a piece of paper draw a set of concentric circles about one-half inch apart (as shown). Make eight spokes, evenly spaced, radiating from the center.

PROCEDURE: To start the game the leader writes four numerals (representing whole or rational numbers) on alternate spokes in the innermost ring. The first player then writes, on the alternate spokes in the second ring, the differences between successive pairs of numbers. He is then followed by the second player writing, on alternate spokes in the next ring, differences of successive pairs of second ring numbers. This procedure continues until the four differences become zero. The player who completes his work first is the winner. It will be found that different sets of

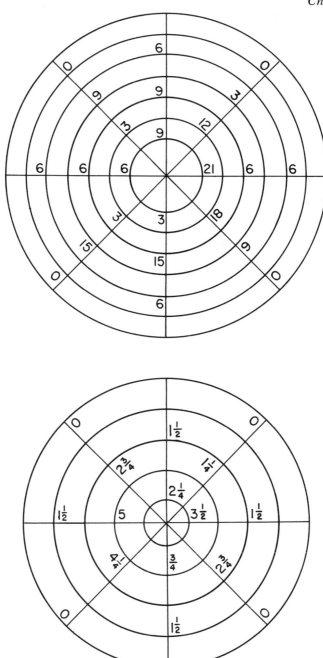

original four numbers will lead to different numbers of rings required, the maximum number of rings required being 12.

The diagrams on p. 136 illustrate two sample play sequences.

3–107. Cross Country Team. PURPOSE: to provide practice in addition and/or subtraction computation.

LEVEL: 2 to 5.

NUMBER OF PLAYERS: 2 or more.

MATERIALS NEEDED: Two sets of duplicated papers on which are shown a road leading over hills, bridges, railroad tracks, detours, etc., with an example to be completed at each place. The course can be the same for each set, but the examples on the practice set will be different from those on the racing set.

PROCEDURE: Players may practice cross-country running until they feel they are "in shape." Then each gets a new "course" face down. At a signal, all turn papers over and race cross-country. Note order of completion. Check answers. Those with mistakes are disqualified. Give awards for first, second, and third places.

3–108. Hunting. PURPOSE: to provide practice in addition and/or subtraction computation.

LEVEL: 2 to 4.

NUMBER OF PLAYERS: 2 or more.

MATERIALS NEEDED: Pictures of birds or animals each with an example to be solved on the back.

PROCEDURE: Hide pictures around the room. Players hunt for "animals." As each is found, the problem on the reverse side must be solved. The winner is the one who finds most animals and completes the problem correctly for each.

This game can be used for practice in solving any kind of problem.

3–109. Animal Tic Tac Toe. PURPOSE: to provide practice in addition and/or subtraction computation and to provide experience with the concepts diagonal, horizontal, and vertical.

LEVEL: 2 to 6.

NUMBER OF PLAYERS: 2 or more.

MATERIALS NEEDED: Flannel board with tic-tac-toe design made with yarn. Felt cutouts of two kinds of animals, e.g., ducks and rabbits (for older children substitute X and O). Cards with examples to solve.

PROCEDURE: Divide group into two teams and designate one animal to each. In front of each player place a cutout of an animal and an example card face down. At a given signal, all complete computations. As each finishes, he comes to the flannel board and places his felt animal on the tic-tac-toe design. The first team to get a row of animals—vertical, horizontal, or diagonal, wins.

For variation, a similar game can be played with story problems.

3–110. Magic Ladder. PURPOSE: to provide practice in addition computation.

LEVEL: 3 to 5.

NUMBER OF PLAYERS: 2.

MATERIALS NEEDED: Playing board with numerals, as in sketch, with holes for marbles or marks for checkers. Twenty marbles or checkers.

PROCEDURE: Players alternate placing marbles in holes to see who can reach a sum of exactly 100 first. Since there are two holes at each place, each number may be included twice.

3–111. Sum Throw. PURPOSE: to provide practice in addition computation.

LEVEL: 3 to 5.

NUMBER OF PLAYERS: 2 to 5.

MATERIALS NEEDED: Target board of plywood, 18″ x 18″ x ¾″, with five pegs or large nails. Label each with strips of masking tape so changes can be made according to practice needed. Three jar rubbers for each player.

PROCEDURE: Each player gets three throws from behind a mark six feet from the target, which may be placed in the chalk tray or on the floor. He must add his score. Largest score wins. Vary rules and numerals to suit ability and needs of players, e.g., dis-

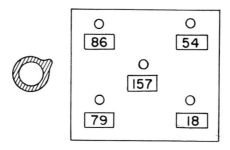

tance from target may be more or less than six feet; each player may be given two or three turns.

3–112. Total Out. PURPOSE: to provide practice in addition.

LEVEL: 3 to 4.

NUMBER OF PLAYERS: 2 to 4.

MATERIALS NEEDED: Four sets of cards, on each of which is a numeral from 1 to 13 (total of 52 cards).

PROCEDURE: Shuffle cards and deal five to each player. Place balance of cards face down on table. Dealer announces totals to be found, any number from 20 to 30. Player to left of dealer begins by drawing a card from the top of the blind deck and checking to see if he has numbers which will total the selected amount. If he has he lays them in front of him in a "book." When

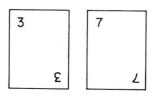

he is through, whether or not he found a book, he discards one card to the bottom of the blind deck, except he need not discard if all his cards make a book. When one player has no cards, he says, "Out." Scores for each player total the number in his books minus the number in his hand; the one who goes out gets an additional amount equal to the value of one book.

3–113. Estimating. PURPOSE: to provide practice in estimating and in computing.

LEVEL: 4 to 6.

NUMBER OF PLAYERS: 2 or more.

MATERIALS NEEDED: 20 to 30 cards each with a large numeral written with a black crayon or felt pen. Numbers selected should depend on practice needed.

PROCEDURE: Shuffle cards. Place five or more in the chalk tray in view of all players. Each gets one turn at estimating the total which is recorded on the chalkboard after his name. Pupils add numbers. The player with the nearest estimate wins. The cards may then be returned to the pack, shuffled, and the game repeated.

Vary by asking for estimates of the average.

For other items which can be adapted to practice on addition and subtraction computation, see numbers 4–35, 6–28, 8–9, 8–10, 8–11, 8–14 through 8–17.

Puzzles

3–114. Thinking skills as well as some practice in computation may be stimulated with this puzzle.

Mr. Hatch, a jeweler, sold a clock to a customer for $6.00 and received a check in the amount of $8.00. Change of $2.00 was given the buyer. Later, Mr. Hatch gave the check to his grocer as part payment for groceries. The check proved to be worthless and the jeweler had to make it good, but the grocer agreed to take a $6.00 clock as part payment. The clock cost Mr. Hatch $4.00. How much did he lose? (The $8.00 bad check cost Mr. Hatch what he paid the grocer, a $4.00 clock and $2.00 cash—total $6.00.)

3–115. Cryptorithms. To challenge fast learners and to stimulate versatility in attack on problems.

Replace letters with digits.	Solutions
a. CROSS	a. 96233
+ ROADS	+ 62513
DANGER	158746

b.	FORTY	b.	29786
	TEN		850
	+ TEN		+ 850
	SIXTY		31486
c.	SEND	c.	9567
	+ MORE		+ 1085
	MONEY		10652

For other cryptorithms, see 4–45.

3–116. To provide a challenge as well as to encourage practice in adding, arrange the digits, 1 to 9, in a magic square. Each row, column, and diagonal must add up to the same total.

6	I	8
7	5	3
2	9	4

Solution:

Children will use a trial and error procedure, but for interested readers, here is one way of making a 3 x 3 magic square:

r − t	r − s + t	r + s
r + s + t	r	r − s − t
r − s	r + s − t	r + t

where r, s, t are whole numbers, $2s \neq t$, and $r > s + t$. (For more on magic squares see numbers 3–89, 3–99, 4–20, 6–15, and 6–16.)

3–117. To provide practice on addition facts and have some fun at the same time, write addition combinations on cards and insert one in each of five envelopes; show the sum on the front of the envelope. On the five cards, no number appears more than once. Name the combinations.

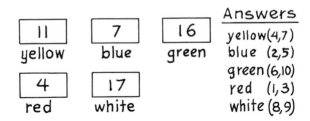

			Answers
11	7	16	yellow(4,7)
yellow	blue	green	blue (2,5)
			green (6,10)
4	17		red (1,3)
red	white		white (8,9)

3–118. To provide practice in solving equations, fill in the missing numerals.

$$
\begin{array}{|c|c|c|c|c|c|}
\hline
6 & + & & - & & =7 \\
\hline
+ & & + & & + & \\
\hline
& + & & - & & =7 \\
\hline
- & & - & & - & \\
\hline
& - & & + & & =6 \\
\hline
=7 & & =8 & & =1 & \\
\hline
\end{array}
$$

3–119. Cross number puzzles (to provide practice in adding and subtracting).

a.

1	2		3
		4	
5	6		
7		8	9

Down
1. $8 - 7$ 5. $8 + 8$
2. $13 - 5$ 6. $12 - 6$
3. $9 + 6$ 8. $3 - 2$
4. $1 + 0$ 9. $5 - 3$

Across
1. 9 + 9
3. 7 − 6
4. 7 + 8
5. 9 + 7
7. 8 − 2
8. 5 + 7

¹1	²8	▨	³1
▨	▨	⁴1	5
⁵1	⁶6	▨	▨
⁷6	▨	⁸1	⁹2

b.

ᵃ1	ᵇ1	▨	ᶜ1	ᵈ3	▨
ᵉ8	▨	ᶠ1	5	▨	ᵍ1
▨	ʰ1	4	▨	ⁱ1	6
ʲ1	4	▨	ᵏ1	6	▨
ˡ7	▨	ᵐ1	4	▨	ⁿ1
▨	ᵒ1	2	▨	ᵖ1	3

Across
a. 5 + 6
c. 6 + 7
e. 17 − 9
f. 7 + 8
g. 9 − 8
h. 5 + 9
i. 8 + 8
j. 9 + 5
k. 7 + 9
l. 12 − 5
m. 8 + 6
n. 7 − 6
o. 6 + 6
p. 5 + 8

Down
a. 9 + 9   i. 7 + 9
b. 8 − 7   j. 9 + 8
c. 8 + 7   k. 7 + 7
d. 12 − 9   m. 5 + 7
f. 7 + 7   n. 8 + 5
g. 9 + 7   o. 6 − 5
h. 6 + 8   p. 9 − 8

c.

a 4	b 2	▨	▨	c 7	d 6	e 3
f 3	8	g 1	▨	▨	h 3	8
i 8	▨	j 1	k 7	l 6	9	▨
▨	▨	m 8	4	2	▨	▨
▨	n 1	3	5	4	▨	o 5
p 8	9	▨	▨	q 3	r 9	6
s 7	8	t 6	▨	u 5	4	▨

Across
a. 126 − 84
c. 1144 − 381
f. 680 − 299
h. 230 − 192
i. 475 − 467
j. 1915 − 146
m. 1095 − 253
n. 2111 − 757
o. 494 − 489
p. 165 − 76
q. 523 − 127
s. 1034 − 248
u. 1040 − 986

Down
a. 987 − 549
b. 490 − 462
c. 873 − 866
d. 767 − 128
e. 529 − 491
g. 7977 − 6794

k. 1614 − 869
l. 73764 − 11329
n. 407 − 209
o. 407 − 351
p. 468 − 381
r. 118 − 24
t. 55 − 49

d.

a 2	b 4	c 8	▨	d 1	e 3	f 5	g 7
h 7	5	3	▨	i 2	8	4	6
j 3	7	9	k 1	▨	l 9	5	7
m 9	6	▨	n 8	3	6	▨	▨
▨	▨	o 4	9	2	▨	p 2	q 3
r 3	s 2	7	▨	t 4	u 8	6	9
v 1	7	6	w 9	▨	x 7	2	8
y 2	6	8	9	▨	z 3	3	5

Across
a. 82 + 69 + 32 + 65
d. 76 + 94 + 837 + 261 + 89
h. 169 + 321 + 189 + 74
i. 923 + 846 + 932 + 145
j. 820 + 860 + 1031 + 930 + 150
l. 186 + 431 + 186 + 154
m. 32 + 37 + 27
n. 175 + 143 + 327 + 83 + 108
o. 109 + 127 + 188 + 68
p. 13 + 7 + 3
r. 107 + 119 + 54 + 47
t. 967 + 846 + 931 + 981
   + 862 + 282
v. 481 + 732 + 349 + 207
x. 333 + 137 + 109 + 68 + 81
y. 732 + 834 + 586 + 537
z. 139 + 79 + 38 + 79

Down

a. 782 + 862 + 532 + 563
b. 781 + 832 + 849 + 927 + 862 + 325
c. 348 + 162 + 199 + 46 + 84
d. 4 + 3 + 5
e. 932 + 872 + 784 + 631 + 677
f. 173 + 133 + 168 + 71
g. 431 + 189 + 88 + 59
k. 73 + 37 + 39 + 40

o. 934 + 847 + 999 + 993 + 995
p. 794 + 689 + 835 + 305
q. 972 + 934 + 988 + 763 + 328
r. 74 + 82 + 77 + 79
s. 84 + 84 + 45 + 63
u. 394 + 288 + 191
w. 17 + 34 + 37 + 11

3–120. To provide practice in adding and subtracting, an array such as the following can be duplicated with signs or numerals omitted. Or, as on the right, with some of each left out.

6	+	8	−	4	=	10
+		+		+		+
9	+	6	−	3	=	12
−		−		+		−
3	+	4	+	5	=	12
=		=		=		=
12	+	10	−	12	=	10

6	+		−	4	=	10
+		+				
9		6	−			12
		−		+		
	+		+	5	=	
=		=				=
12		10	−			10

Making a number puzzle such as this one can be quite a trial and error chore. Try setting a pattern to be followed in both directions. In the above, note that the answers to the horizontal series are 10, 12, and 12, while to the vertical ones the answers are 12, 10, and 12 (the first two are reversed). Now note that the totals are reached by using the same combinations except that the commutative principle has been applied to the first pair in corresponding series. Horizontal: 6 + 8 − 4 = 10, 9 + 6 −· 3 = 12, 3 + 4 + 5 = 12. Vertical: 6 + 9 − 3 = 12, 8 + 6 − 4 = 10, 4 + 3 + 5 = 12.

Shortcuts

The following are shortcuts only if used frequently enough to provide facility; otherwise they should be used only to provide insight.

3–121. Double Column Addition. To add two columns of numbers at one time, add the ones and tens alternately.

$$
\begin{array}{r}
42 \\
27 \\
53 \\
+98 \\
\hline
220
\end{array}
$$

$42 + 7, 49 + 20, 69 + 3, 72 + 50,$
$122 + 8, 130 + 90, 220$

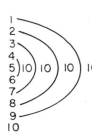

3–122. Sums of Series such as one to nine. A quick way to find the sum of numbers 1 to 9 is by adding the tens and five.

$$(4 \times 10) + 5 = 1 + 2 + 3 + 4 +$$

$$5 + 6 + 7 + 8 + 9$$

Try a similar procedure for finding the sum of numbers one to 19 or one to 29.

3–123. The Sum of a Series of Numbers. To find the sum of a series of numbers the first of which is one, add the first and last numbers, multiply by the last number, and divide by two. The sum of the series one to 12 is $\dfrac{(1 + 12) \times 12}{2} = \dfrac{13 \times 12}{2} = \dfrac{156}{2} = 78.$

Note that by adding the first and last numbers and dividing by two, one finds the average of the series. The sum of a series is the average times the number of numbers in the series.

3–124. Subtracting Nine (based on mod nine; see "casting out nines," number 4–23). To subtract nine from one of the teens, add the digits of the minuend. $17 - 9 = 1 + 7 = 8$ or $15 - 9 = 1 + 5 = 6$.

3–125. Subtraction by Compensation. To subtract numbers which are not multiples of ten, either add or subtract from both minuend and subtrahend so as to leave a multiple of ten. $\begin{array}{r} 48 \\ -22 \\ \hline \end{array}$ may be changed to $\begin{array}{r} 46 \\ -20 \\ \hline \end{array}$, or $\begin{array}{r} 57 \\ -38 \\ \hline \end{array}$ may be changed to $\begin{array}{r} 59 \\ -40 \\ \hline \end{array}$.

Pattern

3–126. Patterns in Addition.

+	**0**	**1**	**2**	**3**	**4**	**5**
0	0	1	2	3	4	5
1	1	2	3	4	5	6
2	2	3	4	5	6	7
3	3	4	5	6	7	8
4	4	5	6	7	8	9
5	5	6	7	8	9	10

1. Counting by one's from either top or left side.
2. Counting by rows of numbers diagonally.
3. Counting by two's diagonally
4. Note diagonal (perpendicular to the one in 3, above), all 2s, all 3s, all 4s, etc.
5. Do you find other patterns?

Verse

3–127. A puzzle in verse form may challenge pupils and provide some practice in adding and subtracting.

> *Johnson's Cat*
> Johnson's cat went up a tree,
> Which was sixty feet and three,
> Every day she climbed eleven,
> Every night she came down seven.

> Tell me, if she did not drop,
> When her paws would reach the top?[10]

Answer: She moved up four feet a day. In 13 days the cat climbed 4 feet $\times$ 13, or 52 feet. Then on the fourteenth day her paws reached the top since $52 + 11 = 63$.

---

[10] *Amusing Problems,* by Harold D. Larsen (Evanston, Illinois: Harper & Row, Publishers, 1951), p. 5.

Chapter 4

MULTIPLICATION AND DIVISION—
WHOLE NUMBERS

FACTS

Materials

4–1. A "machine" to show the relation of ordered pairs to basic operations can be made of heavy cardboard with a pointer to indicate the symbol for one of the operations. Ordered pairs may be "fed into the machine" orally or a set of cards may be made for the purpose. Children respond, orally or in writing, with the number that "will come out of the machine."

See also numbers 3–1 to 3–26, materials for practice on addition and subtraction facts. Most of them can be adapted for practice on multiplication and division facts.

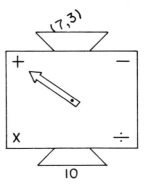

Games

4–2. Feed the Ducks. PURPOSE: to provide practice on multiplication or other facts.

LEVEL: 2 to 6.

NUMBER OF PLAYERS: 2 to 6.

MATERIALS NEEDED: Chart or chalkboard drawing of ducks and of slices of bread on each of which is written a combination which needs practice.

PROCEDURE: Players take turns to see if they can "feed the ducks" by giving answers to all the combinations.

VARIATION: Make chart with picture of ducks with combinations written on them. Make a slot or pocket under each in which cards in the shape of slices of bread can be placed. On the cards should be numerals representing answers to combinations. These cards may be in a bag and may be "fed to the ducks" when the children can correctly match cards to ducks.

4–3. Combination Rummy. PURPOSE: to provide practice on multiplication facts.

LEVEL: 2 to 6.

NUMBER OF PLAYERS: 2 to 6.

MATERIALS NEEDED: A deck of 51 cards with a numeral on each which is either a factor or a product (for addition, use addends and sums); 34 should represent factors and 17 should show products. Select those on which pupils need most practice.

PROCEDURE: Shuffle cards. Each player draws a card; the one with largest number becomes dealer. Deal five cards to each player. Place balance of deck face down on table; turn up one card. Player to left of dealer begins. He may draw either the card face up on table or one from the "blind" deck. He looks to see if he has two factors and a product, e.g., 3, 6, and 18. If so he has a "book" which he may lay on the table before him. When he has played, he discards one card face up. Subsequent players may take all of the cards in the discard pile, or only those on top (or one from the blind deck). When a player has no more cards, he says, "Rummy!" Score is total of numbers in books minus total of numbers on cards unplayed.

4–4. Throw a Fact. PURPOSE: to provide practice on multiplication facts.

LEVEL: 1 to 6.

NUMBER OF PLAYERS: 1 or more.

MATERIALS NEEDED: Design on floor (or on paper taped to floor) consisting of nine squares in each of which is a numeral appropriate to the practice needed. Numbered bean bags.

9	4	6
1	5	2
7	3	8

PROCEDURE: Players stand behind a mark and throw a bean bag onto the squares. If practice is needed in multiplication facts, each player must give the product of his two numbers—the one designated on the bean bag and the one shown in the square on which the bag lands. Standing distance from the squares should be regulated according to the development levels of players. Note that fractional numbers may be substituted for whole numbers. Sums or differences may be given instead of products. Scores may be kept if desired. If only one player, he may try to beat his best score. The number of throws per player should be agreed on before the game begins.

4–5. Product Bingo. PURPOSE: to provide practice on multiplication facts.

LEVEL: 2 to 4.

NUMBER OF PLAYERS: 2 or more.

MATERIALS NEEDED: A bingo-type card for each player. Make cards about 6" x 6" and arrange products in a different order on each card selecting nine of the following: 4,6,8,9,10,12,14,15, 16,18,20,21,24,25. On 2" x 3" cards write multiplication facts on one side and product on the other. Twelve beans or other markers for each player.

4	12	16
15	14	9
21	25	24

$8 \times 2 = \square$

16

PROCEDURE: Select a caller to read equations. Other players place beans on products found on their cards. The first player to get three beans in a row (horizontal, vertical, or diagonal) calls "Bingo!" The caller reads answers as a check. Write the name of the winner on the chalkboard with colored chalk.

4–6. Circle Once. PURPOSE: to provide practice on multiplication facts.

LEVEL: 2 to 4.

NUMBER OF PLAYERS: 2 to 4.

MATERIALS NEEDED: A circular playing board with numerals 0 through 9 arranged at random around the circle. Two or three sets of cards numbered 0 through 9.

PROCEDURE: Place board at center of table. Shuffle cards and place them face down on the table. Players take turns drawing a card and attempting to give the sum or product of the number drawn and each number shown on the board. If correctly done, the card may be kept. If incorrectly done, the card must be placed under the deck. At the end of play, the winner is the one with most cards.

4–7. Pass Red. PURPOSE: to provide practice on multiplication facts.

LEVEL: 2 to 4.

NUMBER OF PLAYERS: 2 to 6.

MATERIALS NEEDED: Red and blue cards of playing card size. On red ones record an arithmetic fact and reverses, e.g., on one red card show 4 × 7; on another show 7 × 4. On blue cards show answers. A deck is 52 cards.

PROCEDURE: Shuffle cards and deal seven cards to each player. Place remaining cards face down at center of table. The first player draws a card from the deck and looks for a set of cards having a fact, its reverse, and the answer. If he has such a set, he lays it on the table before him; if not, he discards a card face down and play proceeds to next player. Winner is the first player to lay down all of his cards or the one who has most "books" at the end of play period.

4–8. Fill the Squares. PURPOSE: to provide practice on multiplication and/or other facts.

LEVEL: 2 to 4.

NUMBER OF PLAYERS: 1 or more.

MATERIALS NEEDED: Paper and pencil.

PROCEDURE: Each player folds his paper until creases show 16 squares (grids may be duplicated beforehand). As directed by the teacher, each child writes numerals across top and at left side. When all are ready, the teacher calls out the operation to be performed. The players fill in the squares and the first who has all right is the winner, or the names of all who have correct papers may be written with colored chalk on the chalkboard. With a stop watch or a sand clock, a child can record his own time and compete against himself each time he repeats a set.

+	3	4	5	6
3				
4				
5				
6				

−	8	9	10	11
3				
4				
5				
6				

x	2	4	6	8
2				
4				
6				
8				

÷	6	12	16	18
2				
3				
4				
6				

4–9. Combination Tennis. PURPOSE: to provide practice on multiplication facts.

LEVEL: 2 to 4.

NUMBER OF PLAYERS: 2 to 10.

MATERIALS NEEDED: Two sets of flash cards.

PROCEDURE: Divide group into two teams, to be stationed at either side of a table on which are two sets of flash cards. Select an umpire and a scorekeeper (one may be the teacher). The first player on team A holds up a flash card. If the first player on team B gives the correct answer without hesitation (as judged by the umpire), A's serve is broken up and he must go to the back of his row and his adversary becomes server. Should first B player hesitate too long or give the wrong answer, he must go to the end of his line; the A player has made a point and continues to serve. At the end of play, the team with most points is declared the winner.

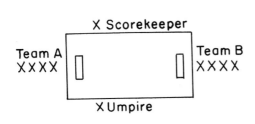

4–10. Who Knows the Table? PURPOSE: to provide practice on multiplication facts.

LEVEL: 2 to 6.

NUMBER OF PLAYERS: 2 or more.

MATERIALS NEEDED: Seven 3″ x 5″ cards for each player. Each card has a product of the table being memorized, or multiplication facts on which practice is needed.

PROCEDURE: Distribute seven cards to each player. Teacher, or leader, calls a multiplication combination such as, "Five times four." The player who has a card with the answer holds it up. If he is the first to do so, he may give it to the leader. The winner is the one who holds the least number of cards at the end of the game.

VARIATION: Provide each player with multiplication tables. All players give correct answers but those who must resort to the table for a given fact must record it for further study.

4–11. Name the Squares. PURPOSE: to provide practice on multiplication facts.

LEVEL: 3 to 4.

NUMBER OF PLAYERS: 1 to 6.

MATERIALS NEEDED: Pointer and a chalkboard table as shown in the accompanying illustration.

X	1	2	3	4	5	6	7	8	9
6									
7									
8									

PROCEDURE: The teacher or leader points at random to a square; the first player gives the product of the number shown above and the one shown at the left. Each player gets three turns. The leader controls time allowed for an answer by silently counting to five. A point is given each player for each correct answer within the time limit.

Name the Squares may be played without competition for points. The leader may simply point to squares at random and players take turns giving the products.

4–12. Multo Scotch. PURPOSE: to provide practice on multiplication facts.

LEVEL: 3 to 5.

NUMBER OF PLAYERS: 2 or more.

MATERIALS NEEDED: A nine-square (as illustrated) or hop-scotch pattern on floor or playground. (May be made on a large sheet of wrapping paper and taped to the floor when needed and rolled up to store at other times.)

4	7	3
9	6	8
2	0	5

PROCEDURE: Divide group into two or more teams. The first player on one team starts at one corner of the pattern and hops on each square; as he does so, he gives the product of the number of the square and a pre-selected number, e.g., five. If he makes no mistakes, he scores a point. Then the first player of the next team begins at a different corner and proceeds as did the first player. When all players have had a turn, scores are totaled; the team with the largest total score is the winner. The game may be varied by choosing a different multiplier after each of the four corners has been used for starting.

VARIATIONS: Sums or differences may be asked for instead of products. For indoor use, players might work their way through the pattern drawn on the chalkboard by pointing to each square instead of hopping.

4–13. Product Race. PURPOSE: to provide practice on multiplication facts.

LEVEL: 3 to 5.

NUMBER OF PLAYERS: 2 or more.

MATERIALS NEEDED: Chalk and chalkboard.

PROCEDURE: Divide group into two teams. Write numerals from 0 to 9 in random order at two places on the chalkboard, as:

3 8 0 2 9 1 6 4 7 5   3 8 0 2 9 1 6 4 7 5

When all are ready, the leader calls, "Multiply by seven," and the first player from each team goes to the chalkboard and records the products of seven and each number indicated at his place. The first player finished with all answers correct scores a point for his team. A different multiplier should be selected for the next pair of players. At the end of play, the team with most points is the winner.

4–14. Multiplication Basketball. PURPOSE: to provide practice on multiplication facts.

LEVEL: 4 to 6.

NUMBER OF PLAYERS: 2 or more teams of 5 players each.

MATERIALS NEEDED: None.

PROCEDURE: Teacher calls multiplication facts to each player on a team, selecting those items on which practice is needed. If all five players give correct answers, a basket is scored and two points recorded. The same procedure is followed with each other team. The team with most points when time is called is the winner.

For other games which may be adapted to multiplication and division facts, see numbers 3–55 through 3–68, 3–70 through 3–76, 3–78, and 3–79.

Verses

4–15. Sometimes memory crutches can be more harmful than helpful. The following verse may amuse children while it makes a point.

A Mortifying Mistake

I studied my tables over and over, and backward and forward, too;
But I couldn't remember six times nine, and I didn't know what to do.
Till sister told me to play with my doll, and not to bother my head—
"If you call her 'Fifty-four' for awhile, you learn it by heart," she said.
So I took my favorite, Mary Ann (though I thought 'twas a dreadful shame
To give such a perfectly lovely child such a perfectly horrid name),
And I called her my dear little "Fifty-four" a hundred times, till I knew
The answer of six times nine as well as the answer of two times two.
Next day Elizabeth Wigglesworth, who always acts so proud,
Said "Six times nine is fifty-two," and I nearly laughed aloud!
But I wished I hadn't when the teacher said, "Now, Dorothy, tell me if you can;"
For I thought of my doll and—sakes alive!—I answered, "Mary Ann!"[1]

4–16. Multiplication (to enjoy a rhyme of multiplication facts).

> One times one is always one,
> Makes no difference how it's done.
> Two times two is always four,
> Always that and never more.

---

[1] Quoted by permission from Lowry W. Harding, *Arithmetic for Child Development* (Dubuque, Iowa: Wm. C. Brown Co., 1959), p. 17.

Three times three is always nine.
Practice this and you'll do fine.[2]

COMPUTATIONS

Activities

4–17. To provide practice in the four fundamentals, choose some-one's telephone number and write it on the chalkboard. Suggest that pupils find how many fives, or multiples of five, (or any other number less than ten), can be found by adding and/or sub-tracting the numbers indicated by the digits. Example: Phone number, 642-3726, could be analyzed as $2 + 3$, $7 + 3$, $7 - 2$, $6 + 4$, $(7 + 6) - 3$, etc. For more advanced pupils, permit the inclusion of multiplication and division as, $(3 \times 7) - 6$, $(4 \times 7) + 2$, $\frac{6}{2} + 2$, etc.

4–18. A set approach to the meaning of multiplication can be had by showing pupils how to illustrate multiplication in some manner such as this:

6×7 may be shown in an array:

The product, 42, may be shown in another array as:

```
OOOOOOO  7
OOOOOOO  7
OOOOOOO  7
OOOOOOO  7
OOOOOOO  7
OOOOOOO  7
OOOOOOO  7
        ──
        42
```

```
OOOOOOOOOO  10
OOOOOOOOOO  10
OOOOOOOOOO  10
OOOOOOOOOO  10
OO           2
            ──
            42
```

4–19. For practice on fundamentals, duplicate a drawing of a grid filled in with one-digit numbers and with operation signs. Vary

[2] Mary Reed, *Counting Rhymes* (New York: Simon and Schuster, 1946), p. 22.

size of grid and operations according to ability of pupils. Children enjoy this different form in which to practice operations.

9	-3	x5	-2	÷7	=
1	+9	x3	+6	÷9	=
8	+7	x2	-9	÷3	=
2	x8	+4	÷5		
7					

4–20. Magic Squares. Making magic squares and/or manipulating the numbers to see if the necessary characteristics are retained may provide interesting practice for many children. (See also numbers 3–89, 3–116, 6–15, and 6–16.)

a. The 5 x 5 magic square may be made by preparing a grid and adding cells on each side as shown in the illustration. Number as with the 3″ x 3″ square described in number 3–89 and follow the same rule in moving outside numerals to inside cells, e.g., move 5 to the empty cell between 13 and 17.

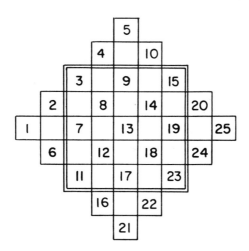

Pupils might be encouraged to experiment by beginning number-ing in any one of the four most removed cells and then noting if the resulting pattern is a magic square.

b. Children may experiment with per-forming operations on the numbers in the cells. Could each be multiplied by three and still leave a magic square? If a given number were added to or subtracted from each cell number, would the resulting square still have the characteristics of a magic square? If divisions are performed and the results included fractions, would this alter the situation?

3	16	9	22	15
20	8	21	14	2
7	25	13	1	19
24	12	5	18	6
11	4	17	10	23

4–21. Some children may enjoy demon-strating their ability to divide by nine by working backward. For example: 660 ÷ 9. First determine the remainder through the "casting out of nines" procedure.[3] $6 + 6 \times 0 = 12$ and $1 + 2 = 3$. Subtract the remainder from the dividend. The quotient digit in the units' place must be a num-ber which is a multiple of nine ending in seven: 27, or 3×9, is such a number. The quotient digit in the tens' place must be a multiple of nine ending in three: 63, or 7×9, is such a number.

A variation which works but may be difficult to explain is as follows (see illustration on p. 163): First determine the remainder by "casting out nines"; $7 + 3 + 2 = 12$; $1 + 2 = 3$. Write the remainder over the digits' place of the dividend.

Subtract the units' number from the remainder $(3 - 2)$ and write the answer over the tens' place. Subtract the tens' number from the number just recorded $(1 - 3$; if this can not be done, add 10 to the first: $11 - 3)$ and write the answer over the hundreds' place.

Subtract as before $(8 - 7$, but remembering that 1 was borrowed, we have $7 - 7)$.

$$9 \overline{)660}$$
$$r3$$
$$9 \overline{)660}$$
$$\underline{-3}$$
$$657$$

$$3r3$$
$$9 \overline{)660}$$
$$\underline{-3}$$
$$657$$
$$\underline{-27}$$
$$630$$

$$73r3$$
$$9 \overline{)660}$$
$$\underline{-3}$$
$$657$$
$$\underline{-27}$$
$$630$$
$$63$$

---

[3] One method of "casting out nines" from a multidigit number is to add the numbers represented by the digits; do the same with this sum if it is also a multidigit number, continuing until a single digit is the sum. This will be the

4–22. Fast learners might try long division in which the multiplication and subtraction are performed together with only the remainder recorded. While the subtraction can be performed either by decomposition or by equal additions, the latter may be the easier.

$$9 \overline{)732}$$

$$\overset{r3}{9 \overline{)732}}$$

Example: 25554 ÷ 67

$$\overset{1\,r3}{9 \overline{)732}}$$

$$\overset{381\,r27}{67 \overline{)25554}}$$
$$54$$
$$9$$
$$27$$

$$\overset{81\,r3}{9 \overline{)732}}$$

$3 \times 7 = 21$	$8 \times 6 = 48$ with 5 carried
$5 - 1 = 4$	and 1 borrowed
$3 \times 6 = 18$ with 2 carried	$53 - 53 = 0$
$25 - 20 = 5$	or
and $8 \times 7 = 56$	$54 - 54 = 0$
$15 - 6 = 9$	$1 \times 7 = 7$
	$14 - 7 = 7$
	$1 \times 6 = 6$
	$8 - 6 = 2$
	or
	$9 - 7 = 2$

4–23. When boys and girls have achieved all the learning that can reasonably be wrung from checking computations by various manipulations of base ten numeration, they may find both pleasure and utility in checking by using a finite number system. The two procedures which follow are illustrative.

a. A widely used check on the accuracy of computations, especially multiplication, known as "casting out nines," may be of interest and value to children. This procedure consists of noting the excess of nines (the remainder when a number is divided by nine) in

number of the remainder if the original number were divided by nine. Example: To cast out nines from 8375, proceed as follows—$8 + 3 + 7 + 5 = 23$; $2 + 3 = 5$. Five is the remainder when 8375 is divided by nine. See also number 4–23 the factors, multiplying these, and comparing with the excess of nines in the product, as in this example:

```
  386 (nines excess = 8)          8
 ×68 (nines excess = 5)         ×5
 ────                           ────
 3088                             40 (nines excess = 4)    4
 2316
 ─────
26248 (nines excess = 4)   4 ◄─────────────────────────────┘
```

Since the excess of nines in the product of eight and five is the same as the excess of nines in the computed product, the computation is considered to be correct.

Note that this check will not detect an error due to a reversal of digits. For example, if the product of the computation shown above had been written as 62248, the excess of nines still would have been four.

A quick way to find the excess of nines is to add the digits of a number, "dropping off" the nines as one proceeds, e.g., in the case of 386, 3 + 8 = 11; dropping 9 from 11 leaves 2; 2 + 6 = 8; the excess of nines in 386 is 8.

Another way to find the excess of nines quickly is to add the digits of a number and if their sum is greater than nine, add the digits of that sum, e.g., for 386, 3 + 8 + 6 = 17 and 1 + 7 = 8; the excess of nines in 386 is eight.

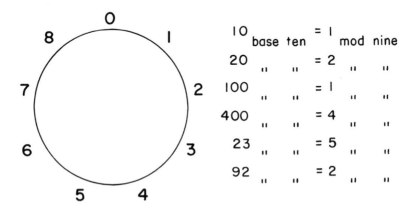

While it is possible to check a computation by casting out any number, one should note that a large number, such as nine or 11, is more likely to indicate accuracy than is a small number, such as two or three. For example, when casting out twos, the excess of an even number is always zero and of an odd number it is always one; this provides some check on the one's place but no more. Since our numeration system has a base of ten, a checking number near ten is most likely to detect errors.

To understand the principle of casting out nines, one needs to understand some aspects of modular arithmetic. Note that the excess of nines in ten is one; also that ten in the whole number system is one in mod nine. The digits of a numeral tell us how many there are of each power of ten, and since each ten would be recorded as one in mod nine, adding the digits of a numeral tells us how the number would be recorded in mod nine. Multiplying the mod nine numbers of a computation and comparing with the answer (also in mod nine) provides a check on a computation done in base ten numeration representing numbers from an infinite set.

b. Modular 11 (mod 11) can be used to check computations.[4] The principle is the same as that of casting out nines above but the procedures differ.

(1)

```
  247      247 ÷ 11 leaves a remainder of 5
× 97        97 ÷ 11 leaves a remainder of 9      5
─────                                          × 9
 1729       45 ÷ 11 leaves a remainder of 1 ⎫ ───
 2223                                        ⎬  45
─────    23959 ÷ 11 leaves a remainder of 1 ⎭
23959
```

(2) Method of even places from odd places:

```
  247     4 from (2+7) leaves 5                5
× 97      9 from (7+11)* leaves 9            × 9
─────                                        ───
 1729     4 from 5 leaves 1 ◀                 45
 2223     (3+5) from (2+9+9) leaves 12
─────     1 from 2 leaves 1 ◀
23959
```

---

[4] See Charles F. Howard and Enoch Dumas, *Teaching Contemporary Mathematics in the Elementary School* (New York: Harper & Row, Publishers, 1966), pp. 80–85.

(3) Method of subtracting from the left:

```
 2 4 7      4-2 =2;  7-2 =5              5
 × 9 7      7-9 =(7-11)*-9=9            × 9
 ─────                                 ───
 1 7 2 9    5-4 = 1 ◄                   45
 2 2 2 3    3-2 =1; 9-1=8; 5-8=(5+11)
 ───────       -8=8; 9-8 = 1 ◄
 2 3 9 5 9
```

✳ Add eleven whenever a subtraction cannot be made

Verbalize the above as follows:

```
 2 4 7      2 from 4 leaves 2; 2 from 7 leaves 5    5
 × 9 7      9 from (7+11) leaves 9                 × 9
 ─────                                             ───
 1 7 2 9    4 from 5 leaves 1 ◄                     45
 2 2 2 3    2 from 3 leaves 1; 1 from 9 leaves 8;
 ───────        8 from (5+11) leaves 8
 2 3 9 5 9      8 from 9 leaves 1 ◄
```

The reason both methods (2) and (3) "work" is that multiples of 11, less than 100, repeat a digit, as 22, 99, 66, etc. Therefore, to cast out elevens from a number, such as 23, one may shorten the procedure of subtracting $23 - 22$ to $3 - 2$. In the case of 247, one first subtracts 22 from 24 to remove the elevens, then 22 from 27; this is done quickly by first subtracting $4 - 2 = 2$, then $7 - 2 = 5$. Method (2), above, simply accumulates (by adding) numbers so as to permit the subtraction to be done in one operation; the procedure makes use of the principle of compensation. (In 247, instead of $4 - 2$ followed by $7 - 2$, one adds $2 + 7$ and then subtracts 4.)

```
 2 4 7
-2 2
 ───
   2 7
 -2 2
 ───
    5
```

For other activities which can be adapted to multiplication and division computation, see numbers 3–82, 3–84, 3–85, 3–86, and 3–91.

Materials

4–24. To help children understand the relations of division to sets and subsets as well as to repeated subtraction, duplicate

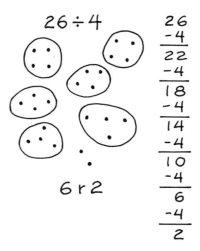

papers on which dots show the dividend. Pupils are to circle sets each with as many dots as the divisor indicates. Counting the sets, they get the quotient and the remainder.

4–25. Preparation for understanding partition division may be facilitated by showing subsets of a given number on a strip of paper which is then folded in alternating directions to separate

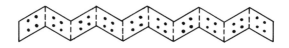

the subsets. The illustration shows there are two subsets of four each in a set of eight; three subsets in a set of 12; ten subsets in a set of 40.

4–26. To help children understand multiplication and division tables, mark the inside of a box lid as illustrated. Cut squares of

X	1	2	3	4	5
1					
2					
3					
4					
5					

paper slightly smaller than the squares on the outline. On each arrange dots to show sets equivalent in number to the products required, as,

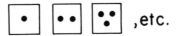 ,etc.

Keep in an envelope. On other squares mark numerals, as

 ,etc.

Store in another envelope.

Children are to place the small papers on the appropriate outline squares, first using the sets of dots and then the numerals.

4–27. To promote the understanding of multiplication tables, provide pupils with large graph paper, preferably with ½″ to 1″

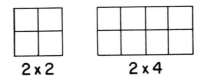

2 x 2   2 x 4

squares. From these children may cut rectangles to illustrate multiplication facts. The rectangles may then be arranged in table sequence.

Cubes of wood or other material may be used in a similar manner.

For other materials useful in teaching multiplication and division computation, see numbers 3–25 and 3–26.

Charts

4–28. Charts can be made to illustrate difficult concepts and remain displayed for reference purposes. Using concrete materials, manipulation and demonstration should precede the introduction of a chart. The following illustrate the two division situations—measurement and partition. For examples of other charts, see Enoch Dumas, Charles F. Howard, and Jean E. Dumas, *Charts for the New Math* (Palo Alto, California: Fearon Publishers, 1966).

Division by Measurement	Division by Partition
How many marbles at 3¢ each can Peter buy for 12 pennies? **4 marbles** 3) 12 We know how many in each set but we do not know how many sets.	How many of Lee's 12 pennies can he give to each of his 3 friends if he gave each the same number? **4 pennies** 3) 12 We know how many sets but we do not know how many in each set.

History

4–29. Lattice Multiplying. (to provide practice on multiplication facts and at the same time develop some appreciation of man's struggle to find efficient ways of multiplying numbers).

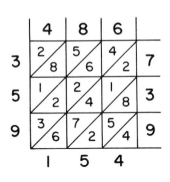

In 1478 a book printed in Treviso, Italy, showed a method of multiplying called the Gelosia (lattice) method. Here is how one would use this method to multiply 486 by 739. Note that in the upper right square is the product of 6 and 7, 42. To its left is the product of 8 and 7, 56. Others are done in a similar manner. The final product is found by adding numbers along diagonals starting with the lower right square, "carrying" to the next diagonal where necessary. The product of 486 and 739 is 359,154.

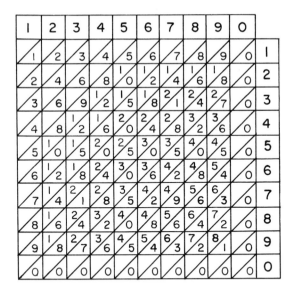

Late in the sixteenth century a Scotchman, John Napier, improved on the lattice method by inventing strips (originally made of bone or ivory and therefore known as Napier's Bones) on which products from a multiplication array were shown. The strips could be arranged so as to make multiplication easy. The array above shows how Napier marked his strips. On the right are shown three strips (and multipliers) for multiplying 374 by some other number, let us say 89. The products of 9 and 3, 7, and 4 are 27, 63, and 36 as shown to the left of 9 as $\boxed{2/7\ 6/3\ 3/6.}$ Adding diagonally as in the lattice method, we have $9 \times 374 = 3366$. Similarly, 8×374 is seen to be 2992. These products should be recorded as $\begin{smallmatrix}3366\\2992\\\hline33286\end{smallmatrix}$ and added in the usual way.

4–30. Galley Method of Dividing. (to provide practice in performing division of numbers, insight regarding the process, and historical appreciation).

The galley method of dividing is an adaption of a Hindu procedure. It was used in Europe from the twelfth to the seventeenth centuries. To divide 10215 by 37 proceed as follows:

a. Write the divisor under the dividend. Determine the first quotient figure by mentally dividing 102 by 37; write 2 to the right.

b. $2 \times 3 = 6$; cross out 3 of 37. $10 - 6 = 4$; cross out 10 and write 4 above it. $2 \times 7 = 14$; cross out 7 of 37; cross out 42 and write 28 $(42 - 14 = 28)$.

c. Rewrite the divisor one place to the right. Determine second quotient figure by mentally dividing 281 by 37; write 7. $7 \times 3 = 21$; cross out 3. $28 - 21 = 7$; cross out 28 and write 7. $7 \times 7 = 49$; cross out 7. $71 - 49 = 22$; cross out 71 and write 22.

d. Rewrite divisor one place to the right. Determine third quotient figure by mentally dividing 225 by 37; write 6. $6 \times 3 = 18$; cross out 3. $22 - 18 = 4$; cross out 22 and write 4. $6 \times 7 = 42$; cross out 7. $45 - 42 = 3$; cross out 45. Remainder is 3.

4–31. Halving and Doubling. (to enjoy an unusual method of multiplying in which one only needs to know how to multiply and to divide by two. Also to provide some historical appreciation of arithmetic.) A multiplication procedure employing halving and doubling was once common. To multiply 42 × 294, write the two numerals and successively divide 42 by 2 and multiply 294 by 2 (ignore remainders). Cross out both numerals if the halved one is even (42, 10, 2). Add remaining numbers on the right; 42 × 294 = 12, 348. If 42 is written in base two it would be 101010 or (1 × 32) + (0 × 16) + (1 × 8) + (0 × 4) + (1 × 2) + (0 × 1). Note that 32 × 294 = 9408; 8 × 294 = 2352; 2 × 294 = 588; and that 32 + 8 + 2 = 42. The crossed out numerals were the ones in which base two zeros occurred in the rewriting of 42.

The doubling was done on an abacus as 294 + 294 = 588; 588 + 588 = 1176; etc.

A variation of the above is to double both columns beginning on the left with one and proceeding until there are numbers in the left column which will total exactly 42. Note that in doubling beginning with one, we will write the binary numeration place values.

~~1~~	~~294~~
2	588
~~4~~	~~1176~~
8	2352
~~16~~	~~4704~~
32	9407
42	12,348

4–32. Finger Multiplying. (to enjoy an historical multiplying procedure in which one needs to know only the facts to five). Once common, finger multiplying is fun to use if one forgets the products of pairs of numbers between five and ten, e.g., 6 × 8. Think: eight is three more than five and six is one more than five. Bend down three fingers on the left hand and one finger on the right hand. The number of fingers bent down (3 + 1) tells the tens' digit (4). The product of the number of unbent fingers on each hand (2 × 4) tells the ones' digit (8). 6 × 8 = 48.

A variation is to give numbers to the fingers of each hand beginning with "6" for the thumb. To multiply 8 × 7, place the "8" finger of one hand against the "7" finger of the other hand, holding the hands with thumbs up. Bend down the fingers below the

"8" and "7" fingers. Count the pointed fingers (the two touching and those above them) for the tens' digit and multiply the number of bent fingers on one hand by the number of bent fingers on the other hand for the ones' digit.

$$3 + 2 = 5$$
$$2 \times 3 = 6$$
$$8 \times 7 = 56$$

Another variety of hand multiplication is used to show the multiplication facts involving nine as one factor. In this instance, number the fingers of both hands from one to ten (one to five on one hand and six to ten on the other). To show 3×9, bend down finger number 3; the two fingers on one side of the bent finger tell the tens and those on the other (seven) tell the ones.

Games

4–33. Times and Plus. PURPOSE: to provide practice in finding various ways in which numbers can be illustrated with Cuisenaire rods.

LEVEL: 2 to 4.

NUMBER OF PLAYERS: 1 or more.

MATERIALS NEEDED: Cuisenaire rods.[5] Paper and pencil.

PROCEDURE: Distribute materials to each player. Explain that when the leader writes a numeral on the chalkboard (or holds up a card on which the numeral is written), each player is to see how many patterns or combinations, including both multiplication and addition, he can find, e.g., if the numeral shown is 8, players may show groupings such as $(2 \times 2) \times 2$, $(2 \times 3) + 2$, 2×4, $(5 \times 1) + (2 + 1)$, etc. Score for each player is the number of combinations shown.

4–34. Do You Match Me? PURPOSE: to provide practice on multiplication and division facts, and on the use of parentheses and brackets in the interpretation of mathematical expressions.

---
[5] See number 2–8.

LEVEL: 2 to 5.

NUMBER OF PLAYERS: 6 or more (or 1 or 2—see variation below).

MATERIALS NEEDED: A set of cards, each containing a numerical expression for some number and each number being named by three different cards. Three cards naming five might be

$$\boxed{[\ 12 \div (2+2)\ ] + 2}\ , \quad \boxed{(2 \times 2) + (2 \div 2)}, \quad \boxed{(3 \times 7) - (4 \times 4)}$$

PROCEDURE: Distribute the cards to the class, one card to each pupil. Should there be one or two pupils over a multiple of three then designate them as referee(s) for that game. Next game's referees may be chosen from the winning group of the previous game.

At a signal the pupils are to move around the room examining other pupils' cards until each finds the other two students having cards naming the same number as his own card. As each group of three gets so assembled it should report to the referee for checking of cards and then go to some designated place in the room. The first group to finish and have cards checked is declared the winner of that game. The cards can then be collected, shuffled, and redistributed for another game. After several games the pupil who has been a member of the most winning groups may be designated the individual winner.

VARIATION: One or two children can play this game by grouping cards that name the same number and then giving these to the teacher for checking.

4–35. Checkout. PURPOSE: to provide practice on multiplication and other facts.

LEVEL: 3 to 5.

NUMBER OF PLAYERS: 1 or more.

MATERIALS NEEDED: A figure for each player such as the one shown. Use fewer and smaller numbers for beginners.

PROCEDURE: Players fill in blanks. Then add numbers represented in each row and in each column. The sum of the totals for the rows and the sum of the totals for the columns should be

	x 4	+ 6	−9	Total
4	16	22	13	51
6	24	30	21	75
5	20	26	17	63
3	12	18	9	39
7	28	34	23	85
Total	100	130	83	313

equal. Generally, the pleasure of this game comes from finding the key total rather than from competition.

For variation, alter the numbers and the order of operations.

4–36. Gold Brick. PURPOSE: to provide practice on division facts and to see that numbers have different names.

LEVEL: 3 to 5.

NUMBER OF PLAYERS: 2 to 6.

MATERIALS NEEDED: A deck of 52 cards consisting of five sets of division facts, nine each with quotients of 5, 6, 7, 8, and 9, e.g., $10 \div 2$, $1 \times \square = 5$, $25 \div 5$, $\square \times 3 = 15$, $20 \div 4$, $\dfrac{30}{6}$, $45 \div 9$, $8 \times \square = 40$, $50 \div 10$. Seven cards have "gold bricks" on them. (If you do not have gold paint, a rectangle can be drawn and "gold" written on it.)

PROCEDURE: Shuffle the cards and deal five to each player; place balance of cards face down in the center of the table. The first player chooses one of his cards, gives the answer, and lays it down at the center of the table. The next player must place a card with the same quotient on the first card played. If he cannot, he may play a "gold brick" and change the suit. Should a player be unable either to follow suit or to play a gold brick, he must draw from the center deck until he can play. The first person to dispose of all his cards is the winner.

4–37. Factor Clap. PURPOSE: to provide practice in multiplying.

LEVEL: 3 to 5.

NUMBER OF PLAYERS: 2 or more.

MATERIALS NEEDED: None.

PROCEDURE: Players alternate counting. When one comes to a predetermined number, such as 6, he claps his hand instead of saying the word. Thereafter clapping must be done on every number of which 6 is a factor, or if the numeral has 6 in it, e.g., 16.

4–38. Tic Tac Multiply. PURPOSE: to provide practice in dividing and in recognizing prime and composite numbers.

LEVEL: 3 to 5.

NUMBER OF PLAYERS: 2.

MATERIALS NEEDED: Paper and pencil or chalkboard and chalk.

6	8	15
14	9	20
25	16	18

PROCEDURE: Draw usual tic tac toe design. Players take turns filling places with composite numbers. First one to find three in a row, horizontally, vertically, or diagonally, which are divisible by a single prime number, wins.

4–39. Assortment Kings. PURPOSE: to provide practice on multiplication facts, and on solving equations.

LEVEL: 3 to 5.

NUMBER OF PLAYERS: 1 or more.

MATERIALS NEEDED: Cuisenaire rods.[6] Duplicated papers with an assortment of exercises such as the following:

PROCEDURE: Distribute papers face down. At a signal players turn up papers and proceed to solve problems using Cuisenaire rods when necessary. Note names of pupils in order of completion.

---

[6] See number 2–8.

When most have finished, check papers. The first three who have perfect papers are listed on the chalkboard as "Assortment Kings for Today."

$$8 + \square = 13 \qquad (2 \times 4) + \square = 12 \qquad 15 - 7 = \square$$

$$15 - (2 \times 7) = \square \qquad 12 - (\tfrac{1}{2} \times 6) = \square \qquad \square - (3 \times 4) = 3$$

$$13 - (\tfrac{2}{3} \times 12) = \square \qquad 14 - (\square \times 8) = 10 \qquad (\tfrac{1}{3} \times 9) + \square = 11$$

$$12 = (\square \times 8) \times 3 \qquad (5 \times 2) + \square = 13 \qquad 14 = (\tfrac{3}{4} \times \square) + 5$$

4–40. Three Guzinta. PURPOSE: to provide practice in multiplying and adding.

LEVEL: 3 to 6.

NUMBER OF PLAYERS: 2 to 6.

MATERIALS NEEDED: A "board" (tagboard or similar) squared off into 10 x 10 or 100 squares approximately 2″ x 2″ in size. A collection of 100 small cards (approximately 1½″ x 1½″), each with a one-digit numeral on it; there should be ten cards for each of the ten numerals, 0 through 9.

PROCEDURE: The game is played in a manner similar to Scrabble with the object here being to form sums that are multiples of three.

Each player is given five cards to start with, and the remaining cards should be placed face down. After each play the number of cards held by the player is brought back up to five by taking the necessary number of cards from the stack. Play proceeds in turn among the pupils with a play consisting of putting down one, two, or three cards onto the board in a line horizontally or vertically so that the sum of the numbers on the cards is a multiple of three. A student may use one or more cards already on the board to form his line of two or more cards. Should more than one line of two or more cards be formed at a play (for example, a line horizontally as well as a line vertically), then every such line of cards must have a sum which is a multiple of three. A line may not exceed five cards in length. A play may be made only in one direction (horizontally or vertically) and the cards making up a line must be on adjacent squares.

Each play scores the total of all lines made in that play. Here is an example of a sequence of plays:

First play: 3, 1, 8
               Score: 12

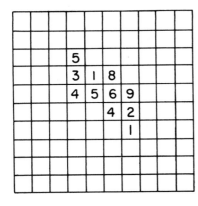

Second play: 5   0 designates
             ③   "already on board"
             4
             Score: 12

Third play: ⑧
             6
             4
             Score: 18

Fourth play: ④,5,⑥
             Score: (4 + 5 + 6)
                        + (1 + 5) = 21

Fifth play: 9
               2
               1
               Score: (4 + 5 + 6 + 9) + (4 + 2) + (9 + 2 + 1) = 42

The game may be continued as long as there are cards to draw from or until some predesignated total score is reached. While each student should keep his own score, it is good to appoint a pupil to serve as master score keeper to keep a running total of everyone's score and to check the score on each play. Vary by using multiples other than three.

4–41. Solitaire Three. PURPOSE: to provide practice in multiplying and adding.

LEVEL: 3 to 6.

NUMBER OF PLAYERS: 1.

MATERIALS NEEDED: Same as for "Three Guzinta."

PROCEDURE: This is a solitaire version of the Three Guzinta game in which the student is in competition with himself, seeking to improve his score on successive games.

The player uses only a 5 x 5 section of the playing board. He draws 25 cards at random from the set of 100 cards and tries to play as many cards as possible into the 25 squares, observing the rules of the Three Guzinta game. Basically, that means that every two or more cards adjacent to each other on the board either in a line horizontally or vertically must total to a multiple of three.

His score becomes the number of cards played. On successive games he tries to improve on previous scores. A perfect game would occur, of course, if all 25 cards were played.

Variations on the play may be had by requiring that sums be a multiple of some designated number other than three.

4–42. Factors Race. PURPOSE: to provide practice in selecting factors.

LEVEL: 4 to 6.

NUMBER OF PLAYERS: 2 or more.

MATERIALS NEEDED: None.

PROCEDURE: Form two teams who line up facing the teacher or leader. The teacher or leader calls a number and the first players on each team compete to see who can first name a pair of factors of that number (excluding one); e.g., if 28 is called, seven and four are expected factors; if 18 is called, either two and nine or three and six are acceptable. The leader may attempt to trick the players by calling a prime number, such as 29. A point is scored for the team from which the first correct pair of factors is heard. The team with most points at the end of play is the winner.

4–43. Equation Scrabble. PURPOSE: to provide practice in multiplication and addition and in their inverses.

LEVEL: 4 to 6.

NUMBER OF PLAYERS: 2 to 6.

MATERIALS NEEDED: Scrabble board or cardboard, 15×15, marked off in one-inch squares. 120 small squares of cardboard each with a numeral (0 to 9) or an operation symbol ($+$, $-$, $\times$, $\div$).

PROCEDURE: Place cardboard squares face down at center of playing board. Each player draws one square; the one who draws the card showing the numeral nearest to 1 will begin play. Replace squares. Each player in turn then draws ten squares and tries to make an equation, e.g., $3 \times 2 = 6$. If he cannot, he may exchange one of his pieces for one from center supply. The next player proceeds in the same manner. Play ends when one player has used all of his squares or when each one has had a specified number of turns. Scoring is as follows: each number in an equation has its face value plus ten points for an addition equation, 20 for subtraction, 30 for multiplication, and 40 for division.

4–44. Multifacto. PURPOSE: to provide practice in recognizing multiples and factors.

LEVEL: 5 to 8.

NUMBER OF PLAYERS: 2 to 6.

MATERIALS NEEDED: A playing board marked off into 8 x 8 squares, each square being about 2″ by 2″. A set of 100 number cards, each about 1½″ x 1½″ and having on its face a numeral at each of its four sides. The numbers represented on the top and left sides are 12 or greater and, in general, composite numbers, while the right and bottom-side numbers are single digit numerals.

PROCEDURE: Deal each player ten number cards. The players play, in turn, a play consisting of placing one card on the board adjacent to at least one previously played card (except that the first play may be made anywhere on the board), so that the numbers on any two adjoining edges are such that one is a multiple of the other (and hence one a factor of the other). The object is to win by being the first to play out all number cards. When a player is unable to make a play with the cards he has, he draws from the reserve card stack (those not dealt out originally) until he can make a play. If no cards remain in the reserve stack and a play cannot be made, the turn is passed.

For a play which joins one edge a score of "one" is earned. When two sets of edges are joined on one play the player scores three. When three sets of edges are joined the score is "five" and when all four sets of edges are joined (a play into an open "hole") the score is ten. The game ends when a player is out of cards; he receives a bonus of 20 on his score. Each player then must subtract from his accumulated score two points for each card he holds. The player with the highest score is declared the winner.

The diagram shows a sequence of play (the circled letter on each card indicates the order in which the cards are played). For

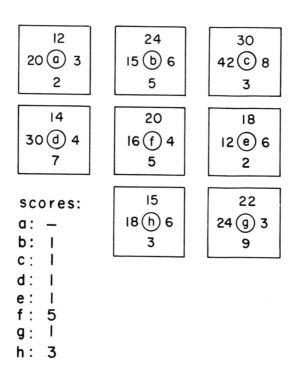

other games which may be adapted to multiplication and division computation, see numbers 6–27, 6–28, 8–10, 8–11, 8–14, 8–15, and 8–16.

Puzzles

4–45. Cryptorithms. To challenge fast learners and give them practice in using alternate approaches to problem solving if one approach does not lead to a solution.

Replace letters with digits.

a.   *Solution*

	ABC	a.		125
	×ABC			×125
	DBC			625
	BCE			250
	ABC			125
	ACDBC			15625

b.   *Solution*

	DEF	b.		105
	×DEF			×105
	FGF			525
	DEFE			1050
	DDEGF			11025

c. Now try this: *Solution*

```
            8                        80809
 xxx)xxxxxxxx            124)10020316
     xxx                              992
     xxxx                            1003
     xxx                              992
     xxxx                            1116
     xxxx                            1116
```

(Any digit may replace a given x.)

The procedure for solving is mainly one of trial and error. For other cryptorithms, see 3–115.

4–46. Cross Number Puzzles.

a. To provide practice on multiplication and division facts.

Across	Down
a. 4 × 4	a. 2 × 7
c. 5 × 9	b. 42 ÷ 7
e. 24 ÷ 6	c. 9 × 5
f. 7 × 5	d. 35 ÷ 7
g. 25 ÷ 5	f. 6 × 6
h. 7 × 8	g. 6 × 9
i. 4 × 6	h. 9 × 6
j. 6 × 9	i. 5 × 4
k. 8 × 5	j. 8 × 7
l. 30 ÷ 5	k. 6 × 8
m. 4 × 7	m. 6 × 4
n. 36 ÷ 9	n. 8 × 6
o. 9 ×.6	o. 40 ÷ 8
p. 6 × 8	p. 32 ÷ 8

The cross number grid (filled in):

a1	b6	▨	c4	d5	▨
e4	▨	f3	5	▨	g5
▨	h5	6	▨	i2	4
j5	4	▨	k4	0	▨
l6	▨	m2	8	▨	n4
▨	o5	4	▨	p4	8

b. To provide varied practice.

¹9	▨	²1	³6	⁴2	⁵6
⁶1	⁷8	3	▨	⁸2	9
⁹6	▨	¹⁰2	¹¹4	2	7
¹²2	¹³1	3	5	▨	¹⁴7
¹⁵9	9	▨	¹⁶5	¹⁷3	2
¹⁸7	3	¹⁹7	7	▨	²⁰9

Down
1. Nine hundred sixteen thousand, two hundred ninety seven
2. 49×27
3. $42 \div 7$
4. 37×6
5. Six hundred ninety seven thousand, seven hundred twenty nine
7. $232 \div 29$
11. 651×7
13. $57 + 136$
17. $1467 \div 489$
19. $4704 \div 672$

Across
1. $774 \div 86$
2. 271×6
6. 61×3
8. $117 - 88$
9. $204 \div 34$
10. 809×3
12. 427×5
14. $84 \div 12$
15. $396 \div 4$
16. 76×7
18. 2459×3
20. $144 \div 16$

c. To provide practice in multiplying and dividing.

ᵃ8	ᵇ5	ᶜ1	▨	ᵈ5	ᵉ5 ᶠ1
ᵍ7	5	6	▨	ʰ7	6 5
▨	▨	ⁱ6	ʲ4	▨	ᵏ9 5
ˡ2	ᵐ3	▨	ⁿ7	▨	ᵒ4 l
ᵖ9	6	▨	۹6	ʳ9	▨
ˢ2	0	ᵗ4	▨	ᵘ5	ᵛ7 ʷ6
ˣ4	0	0	▨	ʸ2	8 8

Across
a. 37×23
d. 29×19
g. 42×18
h. 45×17
i. $1728 \div 27$
k. $1710 \div 18$
l. $1081 \div 47$
n. $336 \div 48$
o. $3157 \div 77$
p. $1440 \div 15$
q. $1587 \div 23$
s. 17×12
u. 72×8
x. 20×20
y. 16×18

Down
a. $1914 \div 22$
b. $2090 \div 38$
c. 83×2
d. $2337 \div 41$
e. 78×73
f. 47×33
j. 28×17
l. 86×34
m. 75×48
r. 34×28
t. $1040 \div 26$
v. $1794 \div 23$
w. $3876 \div 57$

Shortcuts

For a discussion of the use of shortcuts, see Chapter 1, page 16.

4–47. The following method helps children use the decimal property of the Hindu-Arabic numeration system to multiply and divide quickly. To multiply by 10, 100, 1000, etc., add as many zeros to the multiplicand as there are in the multiplier, e.g., 387 × 100 = 38700. This has the effect of moving a numeral as many places to the left of the decimal point as there are tens in the multiplier.

To divide by a power of ten, move the dividend as many places to the right of the decimal point as there are tens in the divisor, e.g., 387 ÷ 100 = 3.87.

Suggestions for 4–48 through 4–58: the following are shortcuts only if practiced frequently and long enough to establish proficiency. In this age of mechanical computers, learning these procedures for the sake of utility may be a waste of time; but some insights with regard to interesting aspects of numbers and numeration systems may well be outcomes when insightful children work their way through the computation methods below.

4–48. Multiplying numbers equidistant from a multiple of ten. To multiply two numbers such as 52 and 48 where each is two removed from 50, square 50, and subtract the square of 2 (difference between 50 and both 48 and 52): 52 × 48 = (50 × 50) − (2 × 2) = 2500 − 4 = 2496.

$$17 \times 23 = 20 \times 20) - (3 \times 3) = 400 - 9 = 391.$$

4–49. Multiplying by factors. Any set of its factors may be substituted for a multiplier, e.g., 27 × 342:

342	342	342	Factors of
×27	×3	×3	27 are
2394	1026	1026	{3, 9} and
684	×9	×3	{3, 3, 3}
9234	9234	3078	
		×3	
		9234	

36×481:

481	481	481	Factors of
$\times 36$	$\times 2$	$\times 4$	36 are
2886	962	1924	$\{2, 2, 3, 3\}$
1443	$\times 2$	$\times 9$	$\{4, 9\}$
17316	1924	17316	
	$\times 3$		
	5772		
	$\times 3$		
	17316		

4–50. Changing a two-digit multiplier to one digit. Sometimes it is easier or quicker to multiply by one digit instead of two, e.g., 18×55 can be changed to 9×110 by halving the 18 and doubling the 55. Similarly, 24×121 can be changed quickly to 8×363 by taking 1/3 of 24 and multiplying 121 by 3. (The principle of compensation is employed; one factor is multiplied by the same number by which the other factor is divided.)

4–51. Complements and multiplication. A complement of a number is the difference between it and the next higher power of ten, e.g., the complement of eight is two because $10 - 8 = 2$. The complement of 45 is 55 because $100 - 45 = 55$.

To multiply two numbers, each of which is a little less than the same power of ten, e.g., 93 and 95, subtract the complement of one from the other (as $95 - 7$ or $93 - 5$), then annex the product of the complements (prefix a zero if the product is less than ten): $95 - 7 = 88\_\_$ and $7 \times 5 = 35$, therefore the product is 8835. Similarly, 992×994: $994 - 8 = 986\_\_\_$ and $8 \times 6 = 48$, therefore the product is 986,048.

$93 \times 95 = (100 - 7) \times (100 - 5) = 10000 - 500 - 700 + 35 = 10000 - 1200 + 35 = (10000 - 1200) + 35 = 8800 + 35 = 8835$. The 88 equals 100 minus the two complements —which is the same as either number minus the other number's complement.

4–52. Supplements and multiplication. A supplement of a number is the difference between it and the next lower power of ten, e.g., the supplement of 103 is 3 because $103 - 100 = 3$. The supplement of 17 is 7 because $17 - 10 = 7$.

To multiply two numbers, each of which is a little more than the same power of ten, e.g., 103 and 106, add the supplement of one number to the other (103 + 6 or 106 + 3), then annex the product of the supplements (prefix a zero if the product is less than ten): 103 + 6 = 109__ and 3 × 6 = 18; therefore the product is 10,918. Similarly, 16 × 17: 16 + 7 = 23__ and 6 × 7 = 42; therefore the product is 272 (note that the 3 of 23 and the 4 of 42 are added).

103 × 106 = (100 + 3) × (100 + 6) = 10000 + 600 + 300 + 18 = 10000 + 900 + 18 = 10900 + 18 = 10918. Notice that 900 is the sum of the two supplements multiplied by 100; therefore, the 109 equals either original number plus the other supplement: 103 + 6 = 106 + 3. The 18 is the product of the supplements.

4–53. Multiplying without carrying.

			4	3	
		3	8	4	
			1	2	3 × 4
		1	6		40 × 4
		2	4		3 × 80
	3	2			40 × 80
		9			3 × 300
1	2				40 × 300
1	6	5	1	2	

43 × 384:

More steps but no carrying

Care must be taken to insure that place value is kept intact. Pupils who have difficulty in this matter may find it helpful to use the straight edge of a card or ruler. Note that in the multiplication example, the addition to achieve the final product is not done from the "front end," though it could be; see number 3–85.

4–54. Averages. The average of an odd number of consecutive numbers is the middle number, e.g., the average of 4, 5, 6, 7, 8, is 6.

The average of an even number of consecutive numbers is the average of the two middle numbers, e.g., the average of 4, 5, 6, 7, 8, 9 is $\dfrac{6+7}{2} = \dfrac{13}{2} = 6\frac{1}{2}$.

The average of both kinds of series shown above can be found also by averaging the first and last numbers, e.g., $\dfrac{4+8}{2} = \dfrac{12}{2} = 6$ and $\dfrac{4+9}{2} = \dfrac{13}{2} = 6\frac{1}{2}$. Note that the rule works with any series in which the interval between numbers is constant, e.g., with 2, 4, 6, 8, 10, the average is $\dfrac{2+10}{2} = \dfrac{12}{2} = 6$; or with 21, 28, 35, 42, the average is $\dfrac{21+42}{2} = \dfrac{63}{2} = 31\frac{1}{2}$.

4–55. Multiplying by 11. To multiply a two-digit number by 11, add the digits of the number being multiplied, and rewrite with their sum as the middle digit, e.g., $27 \times 11 = 297$. If the sum of the digits is itself a two-digit number, write the ones' place digit between the two digits and carry the tens' digit to the hundreds' place; e.g., $86 \times 11 = 946$ because $8 + 6 = 14$.

Note that $27 \times 11 = 27 \times (10 + 1) = 270 + 27 = 297$ and that when multiplying a number by ten, each digit is moved one place to the left as in the algorism.

$$
\begin{array}{r}
27 \\
\times 11 \\
\hline
27 \\
270 \\
\hline
297
\end{array}
$$

4–56. Multiplying by a number almost a power of ten. A number such as 99 is almost 100. When using such a number as a multiplier, first multiply by 100 and then subtract the number, e.g., $99 \times 48 = (100 \times 48) - 48 = 4800 - 48 = 4752$. Similarly, $29 \times 98 = (100 \times 29) - (2 \times 29) = 2900 - 58 = 2842$. Or, if the multiplier is more than 100, add instead of subtract, as: $103 \times 31 = (100 \times 31) + (3 \times 31) = 3100 + 93 = 3193$.

(Since 9, 99, 999, etc., are each one less than a power of ten, one may first multiply by a power of ten and then compensate by subtracting one times the number.)

4–57. Aliquot Parts. If one number is divisible by another, the smaller is said to be an aliquot part of the larger, e.g., 25 is an aliquot part of 100 and $\frac{25}{100} = \frac{1}{4}$. To multiply by 25, one may first multiply by 100 and then divide by four (or in reverse order). $25 \times 32 = \frac{32 \times 100}{4} = \frac{3200}{4} = 800$ or $25 \times 32 = \left(\frac{32}{4}\right) \times 100 = 8 \times 100 = 800$.

Similarly, $\frac{50}{100} = \frac{1}{2}$; therefore, $50 \times 324 = \left(\frac{324}{2}\right) \times 100 = 162 \times 100 = 16200$.

Also, $\frac{125}{1000} = \frac{1}{8}$. $125 \times 400 = \left(\frac{400}{8}\right) \times 1000 = 50 \times 1000 = 50,000$.

$33 \ 1/3 \times 339 = \left(\frac{339}{3}\right) \times 100 = 113 \times 100 = 11,300$.

$20 = \frac{1}{5} \times 100 \quad 12\frac{1}{2} = \frac{1}{8} \times 100 \quad 16\frac{2}{3} = \frac{1}{6} \times 100 \quad 5 = \frac{1}{2} \times 10$

To multiply by a two-digit number in which one digit is the aliquot part of the other as in 24 (two is an aliquot part of four), first multiply by the smaller, being careful of place value, and then by the number representing the relationship of the second digit to the first.

24×4862:

```
 4862        4862 × 2 = 9724
 ×24         4862 × 4 = 9724 × 2 = 19448
 9724
 19448
116688
```

3721×84:

```
 3721        3721 × 4 = 14884
  ×84        3721 × 8 = 14884 × 2 = 29768
14884
29768
312564
```

926×364:

$$
\begin{array}{r}
926 \\
\times 364 \\
\hline
3704 \\
33336 \\
\hline
337064
\end{array}
$$

$926 \times 4 = 3704$. Note that 36 is 9×4
$3704 \times 9 = 33336$

783×642:

$$
\begin{array}{r}
783 \\
\times 624 \\
\hline
4698 \\
18792 \\
\hline
488592
\end{array}
$$

$6 \times 783 = 4698$
$4 \times 4698 = 18792$

Use the above principle in certain division algorisms, e.g., $31298 \div 372$. Here the second quotient figure is an aliquot part of the first (four is an aliquot part of eight). Hence, 1488 is $\frac{1}{2} \times 2976$.

$$
\begin{array}{r}
84 \\
372\overline{)31298} \\
2976 \\
\hline
1538 \\
1488 \\
\hline
50
\end{array}
$$

$$
\begin{array}{r}
36 \\
461\overline{)16596} \\
1383 \\
\hline
2766 \\
2766
\end{array}
$$

6 (in 36) $= 2 \times 3$
$2766 = 2 \times 1383$

Some divisions can be performed quickly by multiplying, using the principle of aliquot parts. Thus, to divide by 25, multiply by 4 and divide by 100, e.g., $462 \div 25 = (462 \times 4) \div 100 = 1848 \div 100 = 18.48$. $235 \div 33\frac{1}{3} = (235 \times 3) \div 100 = 705 \div 100 = 7.05$.

4–58. There are tests of divisibility to help children deal efficiently with certain kinds of problems (e.g., can $463/9$ be changed to lower terms?) and to add some insights regarding number relationships. (Memorizing the rules of divisibility by certain numbers, such as six and eight, may be of doubtful value.) The tests are as follows:

a. A whole number is divisible by two if its ones' digit is divisible by two.

b. A whole number is divisible by three if the sum of its digits is divisible by three.

c. A whole number is divisible by four if the number represented by its tens' and ones' digits is divisible by four, or if the ones' digit plus two times the tens' digit is divisible by four.

d. A whole number is divisible by five if its ones' digit is divisible by five.

e. A whole number is divisible by six if it is divisible by two and by three.

f. A whole number is divisible by eight if the number represented by its hundreds', tens', and ones' digits is divisible by eight, or if the tens' digit plus four times the hundreds' digit is divisible by eight.

g. A number is divisible by nine if the sum of its digits is divisible by nine.

h. Any number is divisible by the product of two or more of its prime divisors, e.g., a number divisible by both two and three is also divisible by 2×3 or 6. A number divisible by a composite number is also divisible by the prime factors of the latter, e.g., a number divisible by six is also divisible by two and three.[7]

Verse

4–59. To provide a puzzling challenge in the form of a rhyme.

> Five times seven and seven times three
> Add to my age, the sum will be
> As many above six nines and four
> As twice my years exceed a score
> From hence, sweet sir, my age explore!

(Answer: $(5 \times 7) + (7 \times 3) + \square = (2\square - 20) + (6 \times 9) + 4$; $56 + \square = (2\square - 20) + 58$; $-2 + \square = 2\square - 20$; $18 + \square = 2\square$; $18 = \square$.)

---

[7] For further explanations of divisibility, see a reference such as J. Houston Banks, *Elementary School Mathematics* (Boston: Allyn and Bacon, Inc., 1966), pp. 87–92.

5

Chapter 5

GEOMETRY

Verse

5–1. Just for fun.

> How doth the little busy bee
> Employ his bee's protractor?
> And, if we worked in wax like he,
> Would our lines be exacter?[1]

Activities

5–2. Develop sensitivity to common geometric figures by having children look for familiar shapes about the classroom or on the school ground. List items reported.

5–3. To stimulate some creativity, outline various shapes of more than one size. Let children cut out shapes and arrange into "pictures" or patterns of their own creation.

5–4. To familiarize children with geometric shapes, duplicate papers on which are two rows of shapes, each of two sizes. Pupils

---

[1] Quoted by permission from *Mathematical Pie,* No. 9, May, 1953, p. 61. (Editorial Office: 100 Burman Road, Shirley, Solihull, England.)

may use a crayon to join those that are alike. Follow with instructions such as "color the circles red" or "color the large triangles blue."

5–5. To help children learn to follow directions while working with geometry, encourage them to draw large shapes on sheets of paper, or duplicate papers for children; four on a paper may be sufficient. Suggest that pupils "draw a small triangle inside the large circle"; proceed similarly with other shapes.

5–6. Encourage problem-solving activities by suggesting:

1. "With paper, paste, pencil, and scissors can you make a box (or cube shape)?" "What other shapes can you make?"
2. "Using pipe cleaners (or straws), how many different shapes can you make?"
3. "Can you draw a design for a house? Its shape could be square, rectangular, or something different. It might have an open central court yard. Try to design a kind you would like." This activity could be followed by one in which children try to construct, using stiff paper, a model of the house each has designed.

5–7. To give pupils a variety of geometry and other math experiences, plan and construct with their help a one-room house large enough for pupils to enter. Discuss shapes, lumber and nail sizes, measure objects needed, count parts—in short, take advantage of arithmetic and science needs generated by the project.

5–8. To give children experience with geometric designs, suggest that children make patterns for floor coverings for a house—patterns for rugs, tiles, vinyls.

5–9. To help children learn about some of the properties of common geometric shapes, provide pupils with strips of stiff paper punched at each end and a handful of paper fasteners. Some of the strips should be the same lengths. Encourage children to make figures of three, four, five, and more sides; then explore the ways in which some shapes can be changed without exchanging strips and what kinds of shapes cannot be changed. Among other things, they should learn that none of the triangles can be changed but that squares and rectangles can be made into parallelograms having no right angles.

Other interesting geometric activities are numbers 7–40 and 7–41.

Designs

5–10. Use ruler and compass to draw an equilateral triangle. First draw the base line of desired length. Then use the compass to make arcs with radii the same length as the base line.

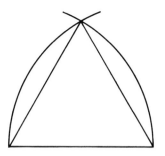

5–11. A square may be drawn by first making a circle. Crease the paper through the center point of the circle. Now fold the paper again so as to make another crease at right angles to the first. Join the points where the crease lines intersect the circle.

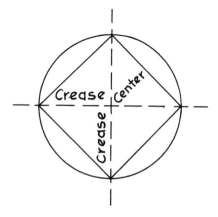

5–12. An interesting way to make a regular pentagon is first to cut a long strip of paper of consistent width. Tie it into a knot and press it flat. The knot part will approximate the form of a regular pentagon.

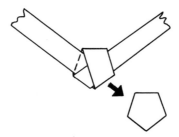

5–13. Pupils may find making repeating patterns of geometric designs an interesting activity. Rulers, compasses, stencils, cutouts, and the like will give children a variety of possibilities.

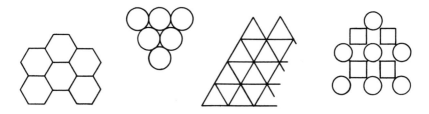

5–14. Designs made with straight lines that leave the impression of curves interest many youngsters at intermediate grades. The

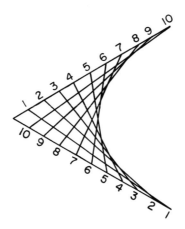

one illustrated is made by marking dots equidistant from each other on each side of an angle, numbering them in opposite orders, and then connecting the dots similarly numbered.

5–15. Some designs may be used to raise questions, as in the illustrations. How many triangles are there?

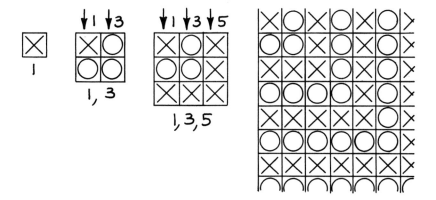

5–16. Some number relationships can be graphically illustrated. In the following design, alternate squares and blocks of squares of increasing size, beginning in the upper left hand corner; show the alternate order of odd numbers. Pupils may discover other relationships or other ways of showing odd numbers as they study designs of this kind.

5–17. Make some models of polyhedrons of construction paper held together with masking tape so children can take the objects apart to see how to make models of their own.

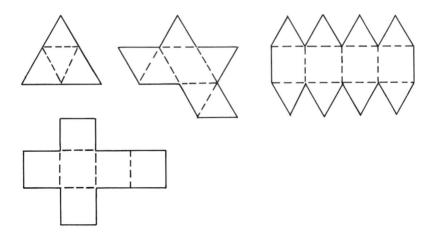

Materials

5–18. For primary grade children, label some boxes "Triangles," "Squares," "Rectangles," etc. Children may be invited to make or find appropriately shaped objects to be placed in the boxes.

5–19. A device for quickly making polygons and many other geometric figures can be made from a square piece of plywood marked off into 25 small squares (five squares each way). Drive a small nail part way into the center of each square. A rubber band can be stretched around nails to form figures desired.

Another useful material for teaching shapes is indicated in number 3–26.

Bulletin Boards

5–20. To interest children in the names of figures, cut a variety of geometric shapes, appropriate to the grade level from colored paper. Provide labels in one envelope with pins in another so children may match shape and name. Include one or more shapes not likely to be familiar. If desired, place blank slips in the label envelope for pupils to print names of shapes and then attach in the correct places.

5–21. To stimulate interest in learning terms, mount on a bulletin board interesting depictions of objects with various geometric shapes (e.g., a baseball for sphere). Near the center, locate a paper on which are printed the names of shapes illustrated. Working as a team, two children may stretch yarn from a word to an appropriate picture. Yarn may be removed at the end of the day and another team attempt to place it the next day.

Mobiles

5–22. Room decorations designed to help children become familiar with shapes can be had if one cuts, with children's help, colored cardboard or plastic geometric figures. Suspend these by nylon thread from slim reeds (or plastic drinking straw, or wire) of varying lengths. Each pair should balance but not with the fulcrum at midpoint. Begin the balancing procedure with the bottom pair. Suspend the mobile from the ceiling.

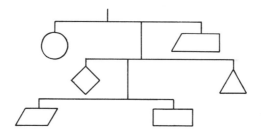

5–23. Do the same as above but with names of shapes on each item.

5–24. Effective mobiles, such as those in number 5–22 above, can be made using three dimensional shapes.

Game

5–25. Squares and More Squares. PURPOSE: to provide practice in noting similarities and differences in geometric figures and in visualizing rearrangements.

LEVEL: 3 to 6.

NUMBER OF PLAYERS: 2.

MATERIALS NEEDED: Scissors, ruler, paper, and pencil.

PROCEDURE: Each of two players obtains a square piece of paper by folding the shorter side of an 8½″ x 11″ sheet onto the longer side and cutting off the excess. He then cuts the square into two odd shaped pieces, rearranges the two pieces by abutting together two edges of the original square, tracing out the figure on another piece of paper, and cutting out the traced figure. This figure is then given to his opponent who is challenged to make one straight cut and reassemble the pieces so as to form a square.

In the diagrams below three examples are given showing where cuts would be made to allow rearrangement of pieces into squares.

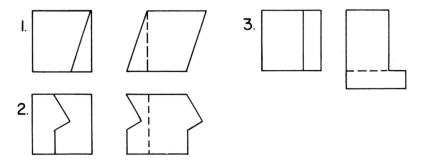

Each player can offer challenges to his opponent until one student gives up or fails to solve the problem in a pre-agreed upon time.

TERMS

Materials

See number 3–26.

Bulletin board

5–26. Head a bulletin board, "Geometric Terms." Then use bright colors in poster paint, yarn, or paper to show examples of items being taught, such as line segment, angle, curve, simple closed curve, circle, polygon, etc.

Mobiles

5–27. To keep geometric terms and/or symbols before children, cut (with pupils' help) colored cardboard or plastic circles, with diagrams and/or symbols of line segments, angles, radii, diameters, chords, etc. Suspend these by nylon thread from slim reeds (or plastic drinking straw, or wire) of different lengths. Each pair should balance but not with the fulcrum at midpoint. Begin the balancing procedure with the bottom pair. Suspend the mobile from the ceiling.

Game

5–28. Name the Figure. PURPOSE: to provide practice in attaching the most descriptive names to shapes.

LEVEL: 3 to 6.

NUMBER OF PLAYERS: 2.

MATERIALS NEEDED: Two sets of 15 or more geometric figures and one with corresponding names. (Suggestions: square, triangle, circle, rectangle, isosceles triangle, scalene triangle, obtuse angle triangle, acute angle triangle, quadrilateral, pentagon, hexagon, octagon, prism, cone, sphere, pyramid, cylinder.)

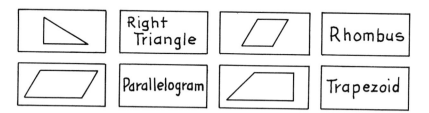

PROCEDURE: Shuffle sets separately. Place cards with drawings face down on table. Deal five vocabulary cards to each player. First player turns up one figure card. If he has the corresponding name card, he may lay both cards before him. If he cannot match cards, he must draw one card. If he still cannot make a match, the figure card is placed face down at the bottom of the deck from which it came. At the end of playing time or when one player has no more cards, the figure cards each has matched are counted. Winner is the one with the largest number.

Verses

For verses intended to aid in the recall of the digits for π (3.1415+), see number 7–48.

T O P O L O G Y

Activities

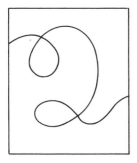

5–29. To provide a simple beginning to topology activities, suggest that pupils "take their crayons for a walk" by starting at one edge of their papers and making a continuous curve ending at the opposite edge. They may then fill in each region in a contrasting color.

5–30. Another kind of simple topological activity can be had by drawing a maze similar to the one illustrated. Children may draw "a short way home" using a red crayon.

5–31. To motivate one kind of topological activity, distribute ten small items to each child. Tell simple stories such as, "Washington had seven sunflower seeds and two boxes in which to plant them. If you were helping Washington, show me how you would arrange the seven seeds in two boxes."

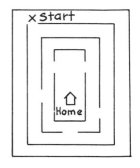

5–32. Many children will be interested in one of the oldest problems of topology— that of the Königsberg bridges. Seven bridges connected parts of the city with two island parks, the latter with a bridge between them. Townspeople became intrigued with the problem of taking

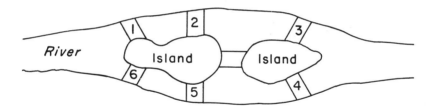

a walk which would take them over each bridge once and only once. Draw a simple map such as that illustrated and challenge pupils to find a path to solve the problem. They may begin their walk at any point. (No matter where they start, they will not make it!)

5–33. Another problem similar to that of the Königsberg bridges described above is that of the house tour in which one is expected to go through each door once and only once. Start in any room and return to that room. (It cannot be done.)

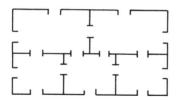

5–34. Considerable motivation for the study of topology can be had by challenging pupils to find ways of tracing the lines in each of the accompanying figures without lifting the pencil or retracing. (Numbers 3 and 4 cannot be done.)

2.

(Numbers 3
and 4 cannot
be done)

3.

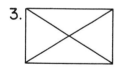

4.

5–35. Challenge pupils to supply electricity, gas, and water to each house without crossing pipes or wires. (This is not possible.)

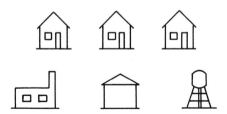

5–36. Geometric figures with variously arranged interior regions present interesting coloring problems. For example, pupils may experiment to see how few colors must be used to color each

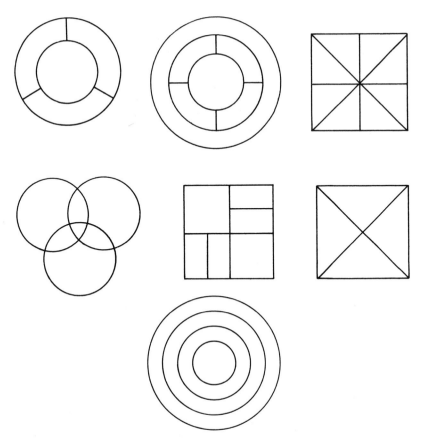

interior region of these figures without having the same color on any two adjacent areas. Challenge pupils to draw a figure requiring *more* than four colors.

5–37. The mystery of knots used in scarf tricks by magicians will interest many pupils. Begin by making a square knot; then weave one end through both loops as shown by the arrows in the illustration. When the ends are pulled, the knot disappears.

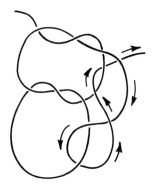

Another knot trick is done by tying two knots loosely in succession on a cord. Work one knot toward and through the other; both knots will remain unchanged.

5–38. Surprising and hence interesting to children is the Mobius strip which is said to have only one side. To make one, cut an 18″ to 24″ strip of tagboard about two inches wide and form it into a loop; but before gluing, give one end a half twist. One may now place his finger at any point on the surface and move it along to any other point without crossing an edge. Permit pupils to check this unusual fact for themselves.

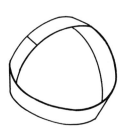

Ask children what would be the result if they were to cut the Mobius strip in two by cutting along the center making the strip now only one-half as wide. After discussion, let someone cut to verify conclusions reached. If the strip is wide enough, follow with a second cut to make the strip half again as wide. Also try making the first cut one-third of the width.

The foregoing represent only a few examples of the interesting study of topology. An activity which might be worthwhile is to arrange for pupils to interview engineers in various industries to learn how topology is used in industry; e.g., how does the telephone company determine the least number or length of lines necessary to connect a given number and location of cities, and how does the highway department gain information essential to the most efficient location of roads?

Designs

5–39. Puzzles made by cutting squares in various ways challenge boys and girls. Use a different color paper for each square so as to identify pieces for each design in case there is some mixing. Place pieces in envelopes available to pupils who complete their work. Triangles, rectangles, parallelograms, circles, or other shapes also can be cut to make puzzles; draw the desired shape on the envelope.

5–40. A task that provides a challenge involves cutting a paper of one shape in such a way that the pieces can be assembled to form another shape. Some examples:

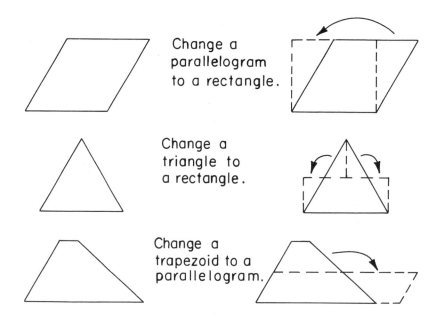

Change a
parallelogram
to a rectangle.

Change a
triangle to
a rectangle.

Change a
trapezoid to a
parallelogram.

Puzzles

5–41. To provide an interesting topological puzzle, make nine dots in the form of a square as shown in the diagram. Draw four straight lines so as to connect every dot; do not mark any dot more than once, or retrace any line, or lift the pencil before completing the drawing.

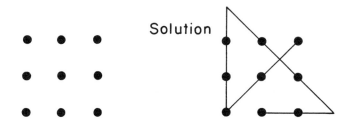

Solution

5–42. To encourage children to visualize geometric puzzles, try this one. If a three-inch cube is painted on all sides and then cut into 27 one-inch cubes, how many cubes are found to be painted

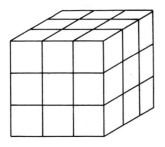

on three faces? On two faces? On one face? On no face? (8, 12, 6, 1. The one-inch cubes with three painted surfaces are those cubes located at the eight corners of the large cube. Those with exactly two painted surfaces are all cubes located at the edges of the large cube less those eight with the three painted surfaces. The one inch cubes with one painted surface are those located at the center of each side of the large cube, and the unpainted cube is the one located in the center of the large cube.)

5–43. To give practice in thinking through a problem, consider a paper-cutting puzzle. Jose cut 2″ x 12″ strips of paper from a sheet 12″ x 18″. Each cut took him four seconds. How long did it take him to cut all the strips? (8 × 4 or 32 seconds.)

5–44. Boys and girls may be interested in puzzles which seem impossible at first glance, as in the following:

Dale wanted to plant ten trees in a way so as to make five rows of four trees each. How did he do it?
Solution:

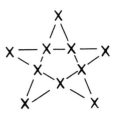

Tricks

A study of optical illusions, of which the following are examples, helps children recognize that the eye is not infallible.[2]

5–45. On a stiff rectangular paper draw ten parallel, evenly spaced line segments of the same length. Cut the paper diagonally in such a way that the cut touches the lower end of the first segment and the upper end of the last one. Now move the top triangle one space to the right. Count the line segments. Are there still ten?

---

[2] For other optical illusions *see* Louis Grant Brandes, *Mathematics Can Be Fun* (Portland, Maine: J. Weston Walch, 1957).

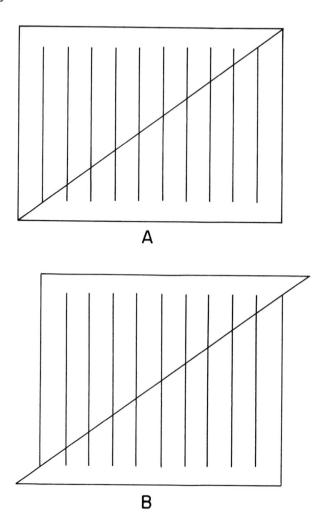

If you measure the line segments in both illustrations, you will see that those in the second are one-tenth longer than in the first. The slightly greater length is hardly visible but the accumulation accounts for a full line segment.

5–46. Many children, and adults too, will be interested in "the case of the disappearing circle." First make a circle at least six inches in diameter on a piece of stiff paper. Next carefully draw

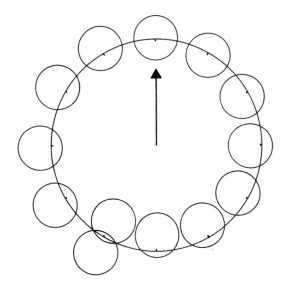

circles equidistant from each other at each of 12 clock positions; proceed so that the inner one at the seven o'clock spot is not quite fully inside the circle. The one at the six o'clock position has a little less of its area inside the circle. Continue in this fashion so that at the one o'clock place the small circle is half in and half out. By the time the seven o'clock position is reached again the small circle is almost completely outside. Thirteen small circles will have been drawn. Now with a razor blade or a very sharp knife point cut along the circumference of the large circle. By turning the circle so that the arrow points to the 11 o'clock position, only 12 small circles appear. What became of the thirteenth?

In the illustration used here, the circles have to be placed with great care. Irregular pictures, as of rabbits, might be easier for showing the illusion.

Chapter 6

FRACTIONAL NUMBERS, DECIMALS, PER CENTS

Activities

See number 3–91.

Materials

6–1. To help children understand fractions and to develop some skill in estimating, place rice, wheat, small beans, or other small items into similar transparent plastic pill boxes so that each has a fraction of a full one: ½, ⅓, ⅔, ¼, ¾. A small piece of masking tape on the bottom may give the fraction. Pupils can arrange the boxes in order of increasing or decreasing size of contents.

Hold a contest to see who can most nearly guess the number of items in each container.

6–2. To help children learn about fractional parts, cut some strips of paper, each a fractional part of a foot. Fold into uniform size but with its designation on the outside, and place in a pocket chart. Children may be instructed to arrange fractions in order of size. If they cannot decide between ⅔ and ¾ for example, they can unfold strips and compare lengths.

6–3. Fractions Equivalence Devices

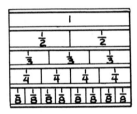

a. On a rectangular piece of stiff paper, draw stripes, each divided into common fractional parts. If desired, color each stripe using thinned water colors. Make as many of these fraction equivalence charts as needed. Incorporate into a bulletin board display.

b. Make separate strips of paper of the same length but divided into various fractional markings as in the example above. Pupils may manipulate strips to compare fractions.

c. Make a frame from a piece of plywood on which narrow strips of wood are nailed or glued. Now make strips of stiff paper of a size to fit between the wooden strips. Mark each strip into fractional parts and cut the parts so that children can place them into position on the board and make their own comparisons.

d. Fractional parts of circles cut so that pupils can manipulate them are useful. If a small piece of coarse sandpaper (or felt, wool cloth, terry cloth, etc.) is glued to the back, the pieces will cling to a flannel board.

e. Sticks a foot long can be cut into fractional parts. Their use helps children learn that fractional parts do not always represent pie-shaped parts of circles.

f. A cube of wood can be cut up into fractional parts to show relationships in three-dimensional pieces.

g. Wooden beads or other objects can be strung on wire and used to show fractional parts of groups.

h. Groups of large flat beans, colored rocks, marbles, and the like can be divided into fractional subsets. Start with some composite number of items such as 36 or 48.

i. Many of the above items can be adapted to illustrate equivalence among common fractions, decimal fractions, and percents.

j. Many other kinds of materials can be used for showing fractional parts of wholes or of sets. Give children a chance to demonstrate their creativity by thinking up kinds of materials to use and ways of using them.

Bulletin Boards

6–4. To acquaint children with fractional parts of wholes, pin a sign reading "Fraction Cracker Box" at the top of a bulletin board. In random fashion pin up tagboard "crackers" marked in wholes, halves, thirds, fourths, or others and some in pieces of unequal size. Number each. Below list some questions, such as: Which crackers are marked in fourths? Which crackers are wholes? Which crackers show three unequal parts? Provide a pad of paper, pencil, and an envelope for depositing answers.

History

6–5. Fractions and Decimals (to help children gain appreciation for man's struggle to adapt the decimal numeration system to represent rational numbers). The Egyptians conceived the idea of fractions and made all but one, $\frac{2}{3}$, as unit fractions (one as the numerator) or combinations of different unit fractions ($\frac{3}{4}$ would be shown as $\frac{1}{2} + \frac{1}{4}$). They made use of a symbol $\bigcirc$ written over the denominator numerals, for example: $\frac{1}{2}$, $\frac{1}{10}$, and $\frac{1}{40}$ would be written as $\bigcirc$, $\bigcirc$, and $\bigcirc$, respectively. Some pupils may want to try forming such common fractions as $\frac{3}{5}$, $\frac{7}{8}$, $\frac{5}{6}$, $\frac{4}{7}$, $\frac{5}{12}$, and others by combining unit fractions; it will not be easy!

We owe our common fraction form, e.g., $\frac{1}{2}$, to the Arabs who introduced the use of the bar; the Hindus had written fractions as 3, or "mixed numbers" as, 8 .
4   1
          3

Not until the sixteenth century did people use decimal fractions as we know them. In 1530, Christoff Rudolff wrote decimals using a bar as we use a point, e.g., 406/78. Common use of decimal fractions followed the publication of a book entitled *La Disme* by Simon Stevin. At first there was confusion as to the symbols to use and we find what we would write as 24.867 in such forms as

$$24\overset{0}{8}\overset{1}{6}\overset{2}{7}, \quad 24867,\ \underset{0\ 1\ 2\ 3}{\ } \quad 24,8\overset{'}{6}\overset{''}{7}\overset{'''}{}, \quad 24\overset{\cdot}{8}\overset{'}{6}\overset{''}{7}\overset{'''}{}, \quad 24/867,$$

$$24/\overset{1\ 2\ 3}{867}, \quad 24/8\overset{\cdot}{6}\overset{\cdot}{7}, \quad 24\lfloor 867 \rfloor.\ \text{or}\ 24\,\underline{867},$$

Even today one finds variations in decimal symbolism; for example, in England the decimal point is raised as 24·867, while a comma is used in Belgium, France, Germany, Italy and others—24,867. (We use a comma to separate the thousands, but in these countries a period is used for this purpose—what we would write as $24,867.50 would be shown as $24.867,50.)

Games

6–6. Half a Rod. PURPOSE: to provide practice in using Cuisenaire rods to show one-half of even whole numbers less than 12. May be used without winners as an activity to discover certain relationships.

LEVEL: 1 to 3.

NUMBER OF PLAYERS: 1 or more.

MATERIALS NEEDED: Cuisenaire rods.[1]

PROCEDURE: Tell players that, at a signal, they are to show all rods or combinations of rods that measure one-half the length of some other rod, e.g., red is one-half the length of purple; green and white are one-half the length of brown. Note that some rods such as black, will have no half-length combinations. Winners are the ones with most correct examples.

---

[1] See number 2–8.

VARIATION: Give rods number values (one for white, two for red, three for green, etc.) and ask players to record on paper all natural numbers or combinations of natural numbers which equal one-half of every even number less than 12 ($\frac{1}{2}$ of $10 = 5 = 4 + 1 = 3 + 2 = 1 + 4 = (2 \times 2) + 1$, etc.). Winners are the players with most correct answers.

6–7. Rods and Thirds. PURPOSE: to provide practice in using Cuisenaire rods to show one-third and other fractional parts of certain numbers and/or rods. May be used also as a discovery activity without winners.

LEVEL: 1 to 4.

NUMBER OF PLAYERS: 1 or more.

MATERIALS NEEDED: Cuisenaire rods.[2]

PROCEDURE: Tell players that at a signal they are to show all rods and combinations of rods that measure one-third the length of other rods up to orange and yellow; e.g., one-third the length of orange and red are purple, white and green, two reds, green and white, four whites. Winners are players with most examples.

VARIATION: Do the same with two-thirds the length of rods up to orange and yellow.

Give rods number values and have players record natural numbers and combinations of natural numbers equalling $\frac{1}{3}$ or $\frac{2}{3}$ of all numbers 15 and less for which natural number answers can be found.

Follow similar procedures for $\frac{1}{4}$, $\frac{2}{4}$, and $\frac{3}{4}$. If consistent with curriculum, children could play these games with fractions greater than one, as $\frac{3}{2}$, $\frac{4}{3}$, $\frac{5}{3}$, $\frac{5}{4}$, etc.

6–8. Rod Comparison. PURPOSE: to provide practice in recognizing fractional parts of wholes. May be used also as a discovery activity without winners.

LEVEL: 1 to 4.

---

[2] *Ibid.*

NUMBER OF PLAYERS: 1 or more.

MATERIALS NEEDED: Cuisenaire rods.[3] Duplicated papers on which are written items such as, White is what fraction of red? _____

"	"	"	"	" purple? __
"	"	"	"	" green? ____
Red "	"	"	" purple? __
"	"	"	"	" dark green? ____
"	"	"	"	" white? ____

Etc.

PROCEDURE: Distribute papers face down. Instruct players that at a given signal, they are to turn papers over and record as many answers as they can before time is called. If one succeeds in finishing all items before the closing signal, he is to stand. When five pupils have finished, say, "Pencils down." Check answers using rods when necessary. Winners are those of the first five players to finish who have correct papers. Those who did not complete their work may now do so.

For another useful game, see number 6–34.

6–9. Name the Fraction. PURPOSE: to provide practice in naming equivalent fractions.

LEVEL: 4 to 6.

NUMBER OF PLAYERS: 2 or more.

MATERIALS NEEDED: A set of three 3″ by 5″ cards for each player. On each card write the numeral for a fractional number.

PROCEDURE: The teacher, or leader, names a fractional number. The player who has a card naming that number must hold up the card and name an equivalent fraction before the leader can count to five. If he succeeds, he may keep the card; failure means that the card goes to the first other player who can name an equivalent fraction. Winner is the pupil accumulating the most cards.

6–10. Equivalent Rummy. PURPOSE: to provide practice in recognizing equivalent fractions. May be adapted to work with

---

[3] *Ibid.*

different kinds of fraction numerals—common fractions, decimal fractions, per cents.

LEVEL: 4 to 6.

NUMBER OF PLAYERS: 2 to 4.

MATERIALS NEEDED: A pack of cards each marked with a fraction. For each number, there must be three cards each with the number shown in a different form, as, ½, ²⁄₄, ⁶⁄₁₂ or ¾, .75, 75%. There should be 18 to 20 such sets.

PROCEDURE: Players draw for dealer; largest number indicates dealer. Deal five cards to each player. Place balance of deck face down with top card turned up. Player to left of dealer begins. He may take either the turned up card or the top card from the "blind" deck. If he has three cards showing equivalent fractions, he lays them before him. When he has finished, he discards one card face up. Play then proceeds to the left. When one player has no cards, the game ends and the one with the most sets wins.

6–11. Renaming Contest. PURPOSE: to provide practice in finding sets of fractions equivalent to a given fraction.

LEVEL: 4 to 6.

NUMBER OF PLAYERS: 2 or more.

MATERIALS NEEDED: Chalk and chalkboard.

PROCEDURE: Divide group into two teams each with a captain. The captain of the first team asks the first player of the second team to rename a fraction, e.g., ¼ may be renamed as ⅛ + ⅛, ⅚ may be renamed as ⅔ + ⅙. Teacher should record response on chalkboard so all players can check. If correct, one point is scored. At end of play, team with highest score wins.

Game may be varied to suit the needs of the group, e.g., decimals may be substituted for fractions, as, .09 may be renamed as .055 + .035.

6–12. Name the Number. PURPOSE: to give practice in renaming whole numbers as fractions, decimals, powers, roots, or in other ways.

LEVEL: 5 to 6.

NUMBER OF PLAYERS: 1 or more.

MATERIALS NEEDED: Paper and pencil.

PROCEDURE: In ten minutes, each player tries to make numerals for as many whole numbers (1 to 100) as he can by using only fours, e.g., $\frac{4}{4} = 1$, $\frac{4 + 4}{4} = 2$. Set the length of time according to the ability of the players. On another occasion, follow the same procedure but select a different number. (Very fast learners may find ways of using decimals, powers, roots, or non-decimal bases.)

FRACTIONAL NUMBERS: COMPUTATION

Activities

6–13. To provide practice in recognizing ratios, duplicate some geometric figures in which regions are congruent. Shade some of the regions. Suggest that children indicate the ratio of shaded parts to unshaded.

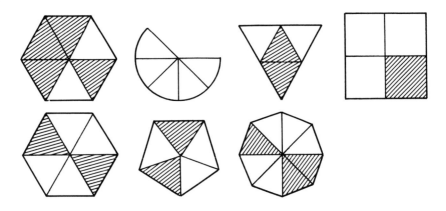

6–14. To provide practice in multiplying fractional numbers, duplicate papers on which pupils are to fill in squares according to directions, as in the illustration. Select items that need practice.

	$\frac{1}{2}$	$\frac{1}{3}$	$\frac{1}{4}$	$\frac{1}{5}$	$\frac{1}{8}$	$\frac{1}{10}$	$\frac{1}{12}$
✕ 2							
✕ 3							
✕ 5							
✕ 10							
✕ $\frac{1}{2}$							
the reciprocal of							
÷ 3							

6–15. Magic squares provide motivation for many children. Multiply each number in the magic square below by ½. Do you still have a magic square? Multiply and divide by other fractions

$3\frac{1}{2}$	0	$2\frac{1}{2}$
1	2	3
$1\frac{1}{2}$	4	$\frac{1}{2}$

and check to see if the "magic" remains. Would it if a given fraction were added to or subtracted from the numbers shown? (For more magic squares, see numbers 3–89, 3–99, 3–116, 4–20, and 6–16.)

6–16. To provide practice in multiplying fractional numbers, suggest that children fill in the cells of the grid illustrated according to these directions. Check to see if the result is a magic square.

a	b	c
d	e	f
g	h	i

a. $270 \times \frac{1}{9}$ (30)   b. $36 \times \frac{1}{4}$ (9)   c. $48 \times \frac{1}{2}$ (24)
d. $120 \times \frac{1}{8}$ (15)   e. $14 \times 1\frac{1}{2}$ (21)   f. $81 \times \frac{1}{3}$ (27)
g. $\frac{1}{2} \times 36$ (18)   h. $231 \times \frac{1}{7}$ (33)   i. $\frac{3}{8} \times 32$ (12)

6–17. To give children practice with fractions, invite each to bring a favorite recipe (or supply one of yours). Write it on the chalkboard or duplicate copies. Suggest that pupils double, triple, or halve the recipe.

Fruit Cocktail Cake

Sift together:
   $1\frac{1}{2}$ c. flour
   1 c. granulated sugar
   1 t. soda
   $\frac{1}{2}$ t. salt

Add:
   1 beaten egg
   $1\frac{1}{2}$ c. fruit cocktail with liquid

Top with:
   $\frac{1}{2}$ c. chopped nuts
   1 c. brown sugar
Place batter in a well greased pan (8″ x 8″) and sprinkle on topping.
Bake in 350° oven for 35 to 40 minutes.

Children of grades K to 4 may profit by having a cooking area available equipped with hot plates and necessary utensils. Here pupils can take turns in the "kitchen" following recipes. The difficulty of the recipes can be adapted to the abilities of the individuals.

For another interesting activity, see number 3–100.

Materials

6–18. To practice recognizing fractional parts of a group, duplicate papers on which there are bars divided into variously numbered parts, some of which are shaded. Suggest that pupils mark after each the fraction telling what part is shaded.

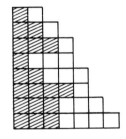

6–19. To provide practice in naming fractions and percent equivalents, or for reference, make a board 16″ to 20″ square with concentric circles. Make a spinner wide enough and long

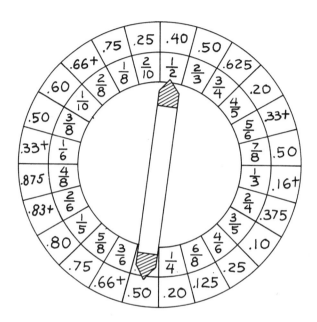

enough to cover the common fractions and point to decimal fractions at one end, and to point to common fractions at the other.

For other useful materials see numbers 3–25 and 3–26.

Games

6–20. Canned Fractions. PURPOSE: to provide practice in adding fractions.

LEVEL: 5 to 6.

NUMBER OF PLAYERS: 1 to 10.

MATERIALS NEEDED: Five low cans, such as size ½ flat, nailed to a board, each with a paper taped to it showing a fraction numeral, as 4½, 9⅚, 3¾, 7⅞, 5⅓. Three small bean bags.

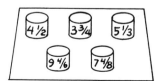

PROCEDURE: Place board with cans on the floor and mark a line ten feet away. Players stand behind line and take three tosses each turn, aiming to get a bean bag into a can. When each has had three turns, he must total his own score. The player with the highest total wins. From time to time, vary the fractions shown on the cans to give practice as needed.

6–21. Mystery Pairs. PURPOSE: to provide practice in recognizing equivalent fractions.

LEVEL: 5 to 6.

NUMBER OF PLAYERS: 2 to 3.

MATERIALS NEEDED: A deck of 52 cards made up of ratio equations with one variable such that two cards will have the same solution, e.g., $\boxed{\dfrac{1}{2} = \dfrac{\square}{8}}$ and $\boxed{\dfrac{4}{\square} = \dfrac{8}{16}}$. There will be 26 such pairs.

PROCEDURE: Shuffle cards and draw for dealer; largest solution number indicates dealer. Deal five cards to each player. Place balance of deck on table face down with top card turned up. Player to left of dealer begins. He may take either the turned up card or one from the "blind" deck. If he has a pair of cards (two with the same solution), he lays them before him. When he has finished, he discards one card face up. Play then proceeds to the left. When one player has no cards the game ends and the one with most pairs wins.

6–22. Mountain Climbing. PURPOSE: to provide practice in solving fraction problems.

LEVEL: 5 to 6.

NUMBER OF PLAYERS: 2 or more.

MATERIALS NEEDED: Chalkboard drawing of a mountain. Set of rational number problems. Paper and pencil.

PROCEDURE: Divide group into two or three teams; give each a name as Swiss Guides, Rocky Mountain Climbers, Austrian Giants. Teacher writes a problem on the chalkboard and players attempt to solve it. At a signal, after several players have indicated that they have completed the problem, all lay pencils on desk. A member of one team gives his solution. If it is correct, each team advances up the mountain as many miles (or thousand feet) as there are players who have completed the problem correctly. Play then proceeds as before. The object is to see which team can climb nearest the top of the mountain.

If the pressure is too great on team members who frequently get wrong answers, change the game to individual mountain climbing. A given child then competes only with himself. Adjust the problems to the needs of each climber.

6–23. King of Fractions. PURPOSE: to provide practice in addition of, or other operation on, fractions.

LEVEL: 5 to 6.

NUMBER OF PLAYERS: 2 to 4.

MATERIALS NEEDED: A set of 52 cards on each of which appears a fraction and a pie shaped illustration. A check sheet showing sums or products depending on operation on which practice is needed. A score sheet.

	$\frac{1}{2}$	$\frac{1}{3}$	$\frac{2}{3}$	$\frac{1}{4}$	$\frac{1}{8}$	$\cdots$
$\frac{1}{2}$	1	$\frac{5}{6}$	$1\frac{1}{6}$	$\frac{3}{4}$	$\frac{5}{8}$	
$\frac{1}{3}$	$\frac{5}{6}$	$\frac{2}{3}$	1	$\frac{7}{12}$		
$\frac{2}{3}$	$1\frac{1}{6}$	1	$1\frac{1}{3}$	$1\frac{1}{12}$		
$\frac{1}{4}$	$\frac{3}{4}$	$\frac{7}{12}$				
$\vdots$						

PROCEDURE: Shuffle cards. Players each draw a card; largest fraction determines dealer. Place deck face down on table. Player to left of dealer begins by drawing two cards and giving the sum (or product) of the fractions shown on the two cards; if needed paper and pencil may be used. He is checked by the player to his left (who uses the check sheet if necessary) and makes a check mark after the player's name on the score sheet if the answer given is correct. Play then proceeds in like manner to the left.

At the end of play, the player with most check marks is the winner.

6–24. What Does It? PURPOSE: to provide practice in recognizing the relation of a given fraction to a pair of other fractions.

LEVEL: 5 to 6.

NUMBER OF PLAYERS: 2 or more (or individuals).

MATERIALS NEEDED: 4″ x 6″ cards on which there are equations without operation signs. For quick checking, record operation sign on reverse side. Examples of cards:

$$\frac{1}{2} \bigcirc \frac{1}{4} = \frac{3}{4} \qquad \frac{2}{3} \bigcirc \frac{1}{3} = \frac{1}{3} \qquad \frac{3}{4} \bigcirc \frac{1}{4} = \frac{3}{16}$$

PROCEDURE: Divide group into two teams. Players stand in parallel lines. Teacher or leader shows a card and first players on each team try to be first to name operation sign. Winner scores a point for his team. First players then go to rear of respective lines and play proceeds with second players. Team with highest score wins.

"What Does It?" could be played also as an individual game. Place equation cards in a stocking box. Include an envelope containing small cards on which operation signs appear. A child matches small cards with equation cards. For checking, the answers can be shown on the bottom of the box.

6–25. Bookmaking. PURPOSE: to provide practice in adding fractions.

LEVEL: 5 to 6.

NUMBER OF PLAYERS: 2 to 3.

MATERIALS NEEDED: A set of cards each marked with a fraction; use denominators 2, 3, 4, 5, 6, 8, 10, 12, e.g., ½, ⅓, ⅔, ¼, ²⁄₄, ¾, ...

PROCEDURE: Dealer sets goal, as ⅞, 1, or 1¼, and distributes four cards to each player. Place balance of deck face down in center of table; turn up top card. Player to left of dealer begins. He adds to his hand either the card turned up or the top card of the blind deck. The object of the game is to see who can combine cards to make fractions total the goal set, e.g., if the goal is 1¼, a player may combine cards with fractions ½, ⅜, ⅜. If he cannot make a play, he must draw cards until he can. Combination cards must be shown to other players; if they agree that he is correct, he may lay the cards before him as a "book." As a player completes his turn he discards one card from his hand to the turned up pile. Player may take all or only the top card of the discard pile. When one player has no more cards or when the blind deck is exhausted, game ends. The player with most books wins.

6–26. Quiz Master. PURPOSE: to provide mental arithmetic practice with fractions—simple addition, equivalent fractions, decimal and fraction equivalents, and the like.

LEVEL: 5 to 6.

NUMBER OF PLAYERS: 2 or more.

MATERIALS NEEDED: Chalk and chalkboard. Toy floor "microphone."

PROCEDURE: Select a Quiz Master. Divide remainder of group into two or more teams. Players suggest categories for mental arithmetic with fractional numbers, e.g., equivalent fractions, addition of fractions, decimal and fraction equivalents, percent and fraction equivalents. Teams huddle to make up five questions for each category, e.g., equivalent fractions: "(1) What fraction is equivalent to ½? (2) What fraction is equivalent to ¾?" When all are ready, the Quiz Master takes his place at the microphone and introduces the first player of one team and asks him to select a category. The captain of the second team then asks a question from his team's list. If the first player answers correctly, he has earned $1 for his team and may try a second question which, if answered correctly, gets his team $2; a third correct answer provides $3 (a total of $6). The first player of the second team is then introduced and play continues as above. At the end of play, the Quiz Master announces the amount of money each team has earned.

6–27. Eraser Bowl. PURPOSE: to provide practice on the addition of fractions.

LEVEL: 5 to 6.

NUMBER OF PLAYERS: 2 or more.

MATERIALS NEEDED: A "bowling alley" marked out on the floor with a three foot circle or oval near one end. Nine chalkboard erasers; on six of them, write a fraction numeral, and place these six in the circle.

PROCEDURE: Divide group into two or more teams. The first player of one team gets three tries at knocking an eraser from the circle using an unmarked eraser. His score is the total of the numbers marked on the erasers he removes from the circle. Play then goes to the first player of the next team. At the end of play, teams total scores to see which has most points.

Many variations are possible, e.g., the eraser serving as bowling ball may be numbered and used as a multiplier; score might be the multiplier times the number shown on each eraser knocked out of the ring.

6–28. Fraction Baseball. PURPOSE: to provide practice in performing operations on fractional numbers.

LEVEL: 6.

NUMBER OF PLAYERS: 2 or more.

PROCEDURE: Draw a diamond on the chalkboard and write two whole numbers, one fractional number, and one "mixed number" along each baseline. Select a fractional number to be used as the "pitch."

Divide group into two teams. The first player on the team that is "up" must add the pitch to the numbers indicated along the first baseline, subtract from those along the second baseline, etc. If

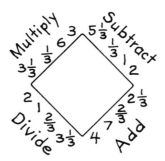

he gets "home" without a mistake, he scores a run for his team. A mistake constitutes an "out"; three outs and the team is retired. The pitch and/or the numerals on the baselines should be changed at the end of each inning or more frequently if desired (such as after a run is scored).

Other games which can be adapted to practice on computation with fractional numbers are 3–104, 3–106, 8–10, 8–11, and 8–21.

Puzzles

6–29. Some children may be challenged by a puzzle such as this.

If water from Mr. Mason's pump can fill a tank in six hours and from Mr. Pitt's in three hours, how long would it take to fill the tank from both pumps at once? (Two hours. In one hour Mr. Mason's pump fills the tank ⅙ full and Mr. Pitt's ⅓ full: ⅙ + ⅓ = ½.)

6–30. Here is a puzzle in which the answer is given but is misleading. Let children try to find the flaw.

When a farmer died, he left 17 cows to his three sons at rates of ½ to Jim, ⅓ to Jack, and ⅑ to Lee. They could not divide the cows among them evenly so a neighbor loaned them one cow. Now with 18 cows Jim got nine, Jack got six, and Lee got two—a total of 17 so they returned the borrowed cow. Neat? What made this possible? (Hint: Add ½, ⅓, ⅑.)

Shortcut

6–31. While the following is sometimes presented as a shortcut, its value is probably greater for providing insight to those pupils who try to understand why the procedure "works."

Subtracting Unit Fractions. To subtract one unit fraction from another, it will be found that the numerator is the difference between the denominators, and the denominator is their product, e.g., $\frac{1}{3} - \frac{1}{8} = \frac{(8-3)}{(8 \times 3)} = \frac{5}{24}$. Changing to lower terms may be desired in some cases, as $\frac{1}{3} - \frac{1}{9} = \frac{(9-3)}{(9 \times 3)} = \frac{6}{27} = \frac{2}{9}$.

The procedure is based on the general statement: If a/b and c/d are fractional numbers, and if a/b is greater than or equal to c/d, then $a/b - c/d = \frac{ad - cb}{bd}$.

Verse

6–32. Some motivation for working with fractional numbers may come from trying to solve this puzzle-problem set in rhyme.

> If to my age there added be
> One-half, one-third, and three times three,
> Six score and ten the sum you'll see;
> Pray tell me what my age should be?![4]

(Answer: $\square + \frac{1}{2}\square + \frac{1}{3}\square + 9 = 120 + 10$; $\frac{11}{6}\square = 121$; $\frac{1}{6}\square = 11$; $\square = 66$.)

DECIMALS: UNDERSTANDINGS

Chart

6–33. To show relationships among certain fractions and their decimal equivalents, make a chart similar to the one illustrated:

---

[4] *Queries and Queeries,* by Harold D. Larsen (Evanston, Illinois: Row, Peterson and Company, 1960), p. 3. Reprinted by permission of Harper & Row, Publishers.

Fractions and Decimals							
$\frac{1}{8}$=.125							
$\frac{1}{4}$ = .25							
$\frac{1}{2}$ = .50							
1 = 1.00							
$\frac{1}{3}$ =.333⁺							
$\frac{1}{6}$ =.166⁺							
$\frac{1}{10}$=.10							

History

See number 6–5.

Games

6–34. Rational Domino. PURPOSE: to provide practice in recognizing equivalent fractions and in adding fractional numbers.

LEVEL: 5 to 6.

NUMBER OF PLAYERS: 2 to 3.

MATERIALS NEEDED: A set of 28 cardboard "dominoes" on each of which are numerals for non-negative rational numbers either as fractions or as decimals or both. Examples:

$\frac{1}{2}$	$\frac{2}{3}$		.25	.75		$\frac{3}{4}$	.50

Make some as doubles, preferably small numbers as

$\frac{1}{4}$	$\frac{1}{4}$	or	.25	.25

PROCEDURE: Place dominoes face down on table and shuffle. Each player selects four; others are left on the table as the "bonepile." The player with the largest double begins by placing it on the table. The player to his left may play a domino if he has one with a number equal to the sum of the two on the double. If he cannot play, he must draw from the bonepile until he can. The next player may play either on the other side of the double if he has the sum or on the last domino played if he has a fraction equal to the exposed end, or equal to the sum of the two fractions. Example:

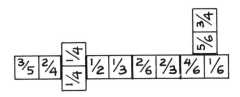

The game ends when one player has no more dominoes. To keep the scoring simple, each player gets one point for a play involving equivalent fractions and two points for a sum; at the end of the game, the winner adds to his score the number of dominoes each of his opponents has.

6–35. Decimal Race. PURPOSE: to provide practice in correctly indicating decimal fractional numbers.

LEVEL: 5 to 6.

NUMBER OF PLAYERS: 2 or more.

MATERIALS NEEDED: Two simple pocket charts and 14 sets of cards with the numerals 0 to 9. Chart made of tagboard 24″ x 5½″.

Fold 1½″ and staple or sew as marked.

PROCEDURE: Place charts where they will be in view of the class but not visible to the contestants. Seven of the 14 sets of cards should be in each of two boxes (arranged in numerical order—seven zeros together, followed by seven ones, followed by seven twos, etc.) near each chart. Divide group into two teams. The first player on each team goes to a chart. The teacher calls out a number such as 248.025 and each player tries to be first to insert the proper cards in the pocket chart. The first to do so scores a point for his team. He should replace cards in his box and in proper order. Proceed similarily with succeeding players. The team with the highest score wins.

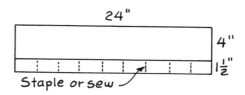

Two other useful games are numbers 6–11 and 6–12.

DECIMALS AND PER CENTS: COMPUTATION

Activity

6–36. A magic square employing decimal fractions may interest boys and girls (See numbers 3–89, 3–99, 3–116, 4–20, 6–15, and 6–16.) Using a decimal fraction of his own choice, a pupil should multiply or divide the numbers in the magic square illustrated. Then try with other decimal fractions. Are the results in each case magic squares?

3.25	1.5	2.75
2.0	2.5	3.0
2.25	3.5	1.75

For another useful activity, see number 7–41.

Materials

6–37. Upper grade pupils may be interested in a device to approximate the answers to certain percent problems. The larger the apparatus, the easier it is to make it precise. Try it this way.

Select a piece of plywood about 27″ square. Make a triangle as shown. The base and left side have 100 ¼″ markings. Drive a small nail at the upper zero point.

To find what percent 30 is of 60, place a yardstick against the

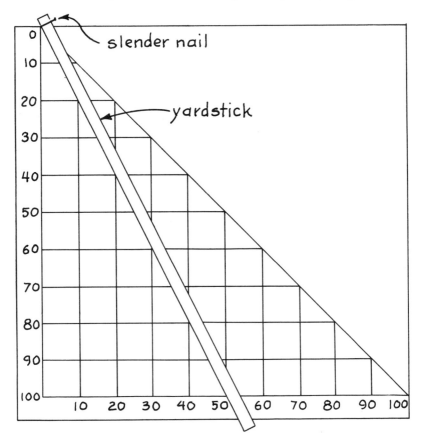

nail with the same side at the intersection of 30 and 60. (Small numbers are read from the base, larger ones from the side.) Reading along the base line one finds the answer to be 50 percent. Of course one may also find other facts, as what is 50 percent of 80 by noting where the yardstick intersects the 80 line.

Game

6–38. Do You Have the Change? PURPOSE: to provide practice with money.

LEVEL: 2 to 4.

NUMBER OF PLAYERS: 4.

MATERIALS NEEDED: Play money as follows: 50¢—8, 25¢—16, 10¢—40, 5¢—80, 1¢—100. Fifty cards each showing purchase amount of less than $1.00.

PROCEDURE: Distribute money to each player as follows: 50¢—2, 25¢—4, 10¢—10, 5¢—20, 1¢—25. Shuffle cards and turn stack face down on table. Each player draws a card; the one getting the card showing the lowest purchase price will play first; return these cards to bottom of stack. Each player in turn draws a card and "makes change" for $1.00; if unable, he must pass. The object is to see who runs out of money first.

VARIATION: Primary children may discard money in the amount of the purchase instead of making change.

7

Chapter 7

MEASURES AND MEASURING

Activities

7–1. To help children learn about common volume measurements, try procedures similar to the following:

 a. Collect milk cartons which are in good condition and of several sizes—½ pint, one pint, one quart, two quarts. Have on hand a bucket of water, glass or plastic measuring pitcher (two-cup size is good), and a towel or two! Tell stories of how much milk was bought at the store, how much was used for breakfast, for after-school snack, and the like. Let children measure to show amounts.

 b. For variation and to help pupils form ideas of quantity, pour the same amount of water into each of several variously sized and shaped containers. Or if this has been done in advance, suggest that children estimate the amount in each container. Pupils should check by pouring into measuring pitcher.

7–2. When weather permits, add variety to the teaching of clock reading by an outdoor activity. Make a large circle (ten feet or more) on the playground and insert the markings of a clock face. Provide two cards on one of which is the word "Hour," and on the other, "Minute." Select two children to hold a card each. Another child may be selected to name a time; whereupon, the two pupils with the cards take positions on the clock face to indicate the places of the hour and minute hands. Other group members check correctness. After three turns, select different children to participate.

At higher levels, pupils may show the time in other zones, as, "What time will a New York clock show when one in San Francisco shows 4:45?"

7–3. Boys and girls improve their understanding of weights if they attempt to estimate one weight equivalent to another. One way to do this is to make or borrow a balance scale. Let pupils place a pill box containing sand of a predetermined weight (may be prepared through the help of a local pharmacist) on one side of the scale. Give children a bag of rice or wheat from which they are to fill a container to match the weight of the one on the scale. They may lift the two until they think the same weight has been achieved. Then weigh to see if correct.

Other kinds of estimation followed by measurements are valuable also.

7–4. To acquaint children with the values of estimation and to develop some skill at it, hold contests to see who can be most nearly correct. Some possibilities are estimating the following:

the number of feet and/or inches across the front of the room
the number of marbles in a jar
the time required to walk around the block
the number of blades of grass in a one-foot square piece of lawn
the temperature of water under given conditions
the cost of a box of groceries of given items
the weight of a familiar object (a large dictionary, the teacher, a
    certain automobile, a particular kind of jet airplane, etc.)
the number of people in the auditorium
the amount of light from a 60-watt lamp
the length of time required for a given conveyance to travel between
    two points
the time needed for light from the sun to reach Venus

the sum of a given series of numbers
the height of a certain building

7–5. Time Line. Making time lines helps children to gain an understanding of the sequence of historic events and some appreciation of intervals of time, the latter, particularly being difficult to acquire and slow to develop. One might begin by helping each child make a personal time line starting with his birthdate and continuing to the present; follow by having children gather data of interesting or important events in the life of some other person such as a parent, a neighbor, the principal, the school nurse, another teacher, etc., and record such data on a time line. Other time lines should be constructed to show, for example, the important events of our city, state, or nation; when children's favorite books were written; the annual winners of baseball's World Series, underlining in red the names of favorite teams; when technological inventions were made; the periods of great artistic achievements; geologic eras; or the sequence of events in space exploration.

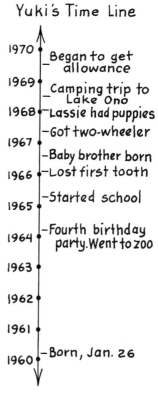

Yuki's Time Line

1970 — Began to get allowance
1969 — Camping trip to Lake Ono
1968 — Lassie had puppies
— Got two-wheeler
1967
— Baby brother born
1966 — Lost first tooth
— Started school
1965
— Fourth birthday
1964   party. Went to zoo
1963
1962
1961
1960 — Born, Jan. 26

A committee of children may find the making of a mathematics time line an interesting and worthwhile activity. Following are some items from among which to select. Reference books may yield others. The first list contains mathematical items; the second some historical points of reference.

a. Babylonian astronomy begins, about 4000 B.C.
Egyptians discover that any triangle with three-four-five dimensions is a right triangle, about 3000 B.C.
Magic square is known, 2200 B.C.
Egyptians are known to use a sundial, 1500 B.C.

Pythagoras discovers the numerical intervals of our common musical scale, about 550 B.C.

Abacus in use, about 500 B.C.

Hindus use numerals, 1 to 9, about 300 B.C.

Euclid writes famous *Elements* (of geometry), about 300 B.C.

Archimedes makes close approximation of π about 260 B.C.

Eratosthenes calculates circumference of the earth, 200 B.C.

360° is ascribed to the circle, 150 B.C.

First use of zero, about 250 A.D.

Buddhists bring Chinese mathematics to Japan, 552 A.D.

Zero and place value are used, about 600 A.D.

Chinese translate a Sanskrit calendar, about 640 A.D.

Baghdad becomes the center of the mathematical world, 700 A.D.

Moors invade Spain bringing Arabic arithmetic with them, 711 A.D.

Al-Khuwarizmi publishes arithmetic book, 825 A.D.

Pope Sylvester II introduces Hindu-Arabic numerals to Europe, about 1000 A.D.

Latin translation of al-Khuwarizmi's book, 1140 A.D.

Rabbi ben Ezra uses equal addition method of subtraction, 1140 A.D.

First Latin book using Hindu-Arabic notation and algorisms is published, 1202 A.D.

Symbols for plus and minus appear, about 1475 A.D.

Gregorian calendar is adopted by Pope Gregory, 1582 A.D.

Napier invents a multiplication device known as "bones," 1617 A.D.

Stevin introduces decimal fractions, 1585 A.D.

Oughtred invents the slide rule, 1622 A.D.

Pascal invents a calculating machine, 1641 A.D.

Pascal writes about the properties of triangles, later followed by the theory of probability, 1653 A.D.

Newton writes his famous *Principia,* 1687 A.D.

French begin accurate survey of Meridian, about 1690 A.D.

First American arithmetic book is published, 1729 A.D.

Gregorian calendar is adopted by England and her American colonies, 1752 A.D.

Arithmetic is required for Harvard University admission, 1816 A.D.

School Mathematics Study Group is formed, 1953 A.D.

b. Chinese known to have stone bells tuned to a five-tone scale, 3000 B.C.

Buddha dies, about 500 B.C.
Death of Socrates, 399 B.C.
Hannibal crosses the Alps, 218 B.C.
End of Greek independence, 146 B.C.
Death of Julius Caesar who helped make the Julian calendar, 44 B.C.
Birth of Jesus Christ, 4 A.D.
Burning of Rome by Nero, 64 A.D.
Invention of paper in China, 105 A.D.
Fall of Roman Empire, 476 A.D.
Death of Mohammed, 632 A.D.
Norman invasion of England, 1066 A.D.
Gutenberg invents printing, 1457 A.D.
Columbus discovers America, 1492 A.D.
Shakespeare dies, 1615 A.D.
Declaration of Independence, 1776 A.D.
Civil War ends, 1865 A.D.
Russians launch Sputnik, 1957 A.D.

Advanced pupils may wish to make parallel time lines of historical mathematical events and of non-mathematical events, and then try to discover cause or effect relationships between events shown on the two time lines.

7–6. To provide practice in measuring, duplicate the following directions for making a drawing on 8½″ x 11″ paper. A ruler and pencil are needed.

Mark your paper N at the top, E at the right, S at the bottom, and W at the left. Begin work one inch from the W edge of the paper and five inches from the N edge. Draw a line segment two inches long in the direction of the S center of the paper. Draw a line segment 4⅝″ long and parallel to the S edge of the paper. Draw a two inch line segment through the right endpoint of the line segment so that point and the point at the center of the bottom of the page are collinear; draw in a NE direction. Draw a line segment westward 6½.″ (This should take you to the beginning point.) Now find a point 2½″ eastward and draw a line segment four inches N. Draw a line segment five inches in a SE direction toward a point five inches S of the NE corner of the paper. Draw a line segment 3⅞″ W. What have you drawn? (A picture of a sailboat.)

7–7. While studying the geography of the United States, give attention to the time zones. A project for some children might be that of looking up the history of time zones. Others might check to see what part of the United States or its territories is in the earliest time zone (where the day begins). What part of the United States is in the latest time zone (where the day ends).

7–8. Studying the innovation and improvement of time keeping equipment is a good enrichment activity.

7–9. Following are some measurement topics for exploration and reporting to classmates:

a. What kinds of clocks has man used? How does each operate? Invent a new kind of timepiece; e.g., could one tell time from a device that counted one's pulse?

b. What kinds of thermometers are there? How does each work? Construct a table to give Centigrade equivalents to Fahrenheit readings.

c. What units of measuring length have been used commonly? How can the thickness of hair be measured? How do astronomers measure the distance between stars?

d. Compare the metric and English units of measuring length. Which do you think is the better? Why?

e. How could one measure the altitude above sea level of your school building?

f. What instruments are used to measure weight? How does each operate? How is the weight of the earth determined?

g. What things can be measured only by indirect means? What are some indirect measuring instruments? How does each work? What is really measured? (For example, a spring scale measures the tension of a steel spring.)

h. How are money values measured in foreign countries of your choice? If prices were the same, what would U.S. items of interest to you cost in each country, if you used its money?

i. How do people measure the following:
   1. The number of calories in foods.
   2. The vitamins in a glass of milk.
   3. The number of atoms in a drop of water.
   4. The number of electrons in an atom.

5. The depth of the ocean.
6. The amount of gold in gold ore.
7. The volume of an irregularly shaped rock.
8. The light falling on your desk.
9. The speed of an airplane.
10. The heat of the sun's surface.
11. The location of the North Pole.
12. The power of a stick of dynamite.
13. The speed of light.
14. The speed of sound.
15. The intensity of sound.
16. The length of a radio wave.
17. The horsepower of an automobile engine.
18. The strength of a piece of steel.
19. The direction and velocity of wind.
20. The wearing quality of a piece of cloth.
21. The value of a diamond.
22. The amount of acid in a cup of coffee.
23. The colorfastness of dye.
24. The age of cave paintings.
25. The amount of oxygen in the classroom.

For other useful measuring activities, see numbers 3–91 and 6–17.

Materials

7–10. A pocket chart calendar may interest boys and girls. Fold a strip of construction paper to make a series of five pockets. Into each, place a pack of as many cards as there are days in a given week. Each card should bear a date number. Add the names of children who have birthdays, and record other special days as desired. Each morning, pupils' attention should be drawn to the removal of a card (or cards). On a child's birthday, give him the card on which his name appears.

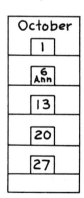

7–11. To record days until some special event, help children make a paper chain of as many links as there are days. If desired, a numeral can be written on each link by using a marking pen. Each day a link (three after a weekend) can be cut from the chain.

7–12. For materials to help teach the use of money, duplicate circles the size of pennies on bright brown paper and of other coins on light grey paper. Mark the value on each. Children may cut out their own and also make paper "purses" by folding construction paper 6″ x 9″ to 6″ x 4½″. Staple or tape the ends. Yarn may be used as straps.

7–13. The following are suggestions for helping boys and girls understand how odometers and adding machines work.

Nearly all children know that the odometer on a car adds the miles (and in most, the tenths of miles) though they may speak of it as part of the "speedometer." Sometimes teachers can get from garages defective speedometers on which the odometer still works and which may be removed for examination by children.

 As readiness for understanding how an odometer works, a model may be made from three or four boards cut into circular sections. On the rim of each, place the numerals from 0 to 9. Bore a hole at the center of each circle and slip onto a wooden dowel so that each will turn independently.

Children should learn that as the wheel on the right makes a full turn, the one next to it is nudged one-tenth of a turn; when the latter has made a full turn, the wheel to its left moves one-tenth of a turn. This is the way an odometer works.

The common adding machine works on the same principle as the odometer. Mechanical devices spin the wheels very rapidly when a handle is pulled or a button pressed.

7–14. Interest in measuring can be stimulated by an activity involving the measuring of the heights of children.

On a strip of paper wide enough to accommodate the variation in heights of pupils plus two or three inches, mark vertical lines, one for each child with his name at the top. Tape the strip to the wall with the lower edge at the height of the shortest child. Note

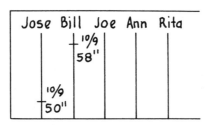

the height from the floor on a corner that each time children are measured, the paper can be placed in the same position. As each child is measured, make a mark on his line and label with the date and height. Roll up the paper and store until time to measure again.

7–15. To give practice in reading a thermometer, make a mock one from heavy cardboard and ribbon. Examine a standard thermometer for correct marking and numeration.

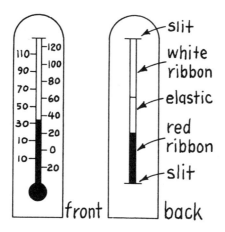

Another item adaptable to practice on measuring is number 3–26.

Bulletin boards

(The following are some suggested bulletin boards designed to stimulate children's interest in measurement.)

7–16. Display a variety of frequently used kinds of nails on tagboard. Near each give the kind and number size.

7–17. Cut out colored paper pieces the sizes and shape of end cuts of lumber. Label as to kind (flooring, siding, shiplap etc.) and size. Perhaps a lumber company will provide you with the real thing.

7–18. Fasten needles and thread samples on tagboard. Label each as to size and kind.

7–19. Make a display of foreign and domestic money according to nearest equivalent. Children may help with the collection.

7–20. Make a display using stamps of countries studied in social studies.

7–21. Make a display of measuring instruments. Label as to name and use.

7–22. With the help of your pharmacist or grocer, display bottles and other containers. Label sizes. In one area of the bulletin board place a table of metric and English measurement equivalents.

7–23. On an outline map of the United States, pin small pennants showing temperatures in selected places of interest to pupils. Change frequently. Daily newspapers often include temperature reports from key cities.

7–24. Mount outlines or pictures of familiar items and indicate the weight of each. Write the question, "How much would these weigh if they were on the moon?"

7–25. Make a bulletin board calendar with all numerals in base five. Change the base each month.

History

7–26. What happened to September in 1752? (To help children appreciate the problems of calendar makers.) The calendar we use today has undergone many changes. For example, December was once the tenth month because New Year's Day was in March. The word, December, comes from a Latin word meaning ten.

Early calendar makers tried having 12 months of 30 days each or 360 days in a year. They did not know that there are really 365 days, 5 hours, 48 minutes, and 49⁷⁄₁₀ seconds in a year. So some special days that used to come in winter came earlier and earlier until they were being celebrated in the fall instead of in the winter.

In 45 B.C., Julius Caesar, who was the emperor of Rome, established what became known as the Julian Calendar. It had 365 days for each of three years and then 366 days the fourth year. This was a much better calendar than any before it, but still it was not quite accurate. And by 1582 an error of ten days had accumulated. In that year, Pope Gregory announced a new calendar and ordered that after October 4 of 1582 should come October 15.

The new calendar was called the Gregorian Calendar. It was not until 1751 that the English parliament accepted the change for England and her colonies. New Year's Day was set for January 1 instead of March 25, and September 2 of 1752 was to be followed by September 14 making a month of only 19 days and with only two Sundays and two Mondays.

The plan of the Gregorian Calendar is to have 365 days most of the years. If the number of the year is exactly divisible by four, it will have 366 days, called leap year. Century years divisible by 400 will be leap years; e.g., 1600 was a leap year but not 1700, 1800, or 1900. Will 2000 be a leap year?

The children should be encouraged to check the dictionary for the explanation of the term "leap year" and figure out how the "leap" works. For example, they will find that a date in March that is Wednesday would ordinarily fall on Thursday the following year, but if the next year were leap year, it will "leap" over Thursday and fall on Friday.

7–27. What Day of the Week Was It? (To help children gain interest in studying calendar problems.)

A German mathematician, Carl F. Gauss (1777–1855), determined a way to find the day of the week for any given date. The procedure is a bit complicated by the calendar changes and leap years. Following is a less difficult device through which pupils may compute the day of the week for any date in American history.

To find the day of the week for Judy's birthday, May 18, 1945, consider the last two digits of the year (45); add ¼ of this to it, disregarding the remainder, $(45 + 11 = 56)$; add the month number from Table I $(56 + 2 = 58)$; add the day of the month $(58 + 18 = 76)$; add the year number from Table II $(76 + 0 = 76)$; divide by seven and note the remainder $(76 \div 7 = 10\,r\,6)$; determine the day of the week by applying the remainder to Table III (6 is Friday).

Table I		*Table II*		*Table III*	
January	1	1900 to 2000	0	Sunday	1
(If leap year)	0	1800 to 1900	2	Monday	2
February	4	Sept. 14, 1752			
(If leap year)	3	to 1800	4	Tuesday	3
March	4	1700 to Sept. 2,			
		1752	1	Wednesday	4
April	0	1600–1700	2	Thursday	5
May	2			Friday	6
June	5			Saturday	7
July	0				
August	3				
September	6				
October	1				
November	4				
December	6				

Games

7–28. Measurement Bingo. PURPOSE: to provide practice in relating measuring terms to measuring instruments.

LEVEL: 3 to 5.

NUMBER OF PLAYERS: 2 or more.

MATERIALS NEEDED: Nine 8½ " x 11" cards on which are pictures or drawings of measuring instruments (suggestions: scale, ruler, yardstick, measuring cup, thermometer, clock, calendar, speedometer, odometer, protractor, pedometer). Bingo-type cards for players using nine squares in each of which is the name of a unit of measure arranged differently on each card; some cards have words not related to pictures. Nine beans or other markers for each player.

angles	pounds	yards
ounces	miles	minutes
miles per hour	days	degrees

PROCEDURE: Distribute bingo cards and markers to players. Leader holds up a picture card and pupils who have a word indicating a unit measured by the pictured item place a marker in the appropriate square. Player getting three markers in a row either vertically or horizontally calls out "Bingo" and is the winner of that round. Players exchange cards and leader shuffles picture cards after which another game may be played.

7–29. What's Your Hurry? PURPOSE: to give practice in computing travel speed.

LEVEL: 5 to 6.

NUMBER OF PLAYERS: Sets of 3.

Time

MATERIALS NEEDED: Two clocklike circles for each set of three players. Paper and pencil.

PROCEDURE: Divide group into sets of three; designate each player as A, B, or C. To begin play, A sets clock to indicate time, B sets distance, and C calculates rate. A and B check for accuracy; if they agree with C, the latter gets a point. Play continues as before except in the order B, C, A; then C, A, B, etc.

Distance

At end of playing time, the member of each set with the most points wins.

Verses

7–30. To help children remember the number of days in each month.

> Thirty Days hath September,
> April, June, and November;
> All the rest have thirty-one,
> Save February, which has twenty-eight in fine,
> And leap year brings it twenty-nine.[1]

7–31. To enjoy. There must be an easier way to learn the names of the days of the week!

> *Monday's Child*
>
> Monday's child is fair of face,
> Tuesday's child is full of grace,
> Wednesday's child is full of woe,
> Thursday's child has far to go,
> Friday's child is loving and giving,
> Saturday's child must work hard for a living,
> But the child that is born on the Sabbath day
> Is blithe and winsome and happy and gay.[2]

7–32. To add interest to a review of common measurements.

> Arithmetic in school today
> Will be a jolly time.
> Every question teacher asks
> Please answer her in rhyme.
>
> The teacher said, "Now listen, class,
> The question isn't hard.
> There are twelve inches in a foot
> And three feet in a _____ (yard).
>
> The minute hand around the clock,
> Gives sixty minutes and no more.
> The hour hand throughout the day,
> Will give us hours _____ (24).

---

[1] Mary Reed, *Counting Rhymes*, (New York: Simon and Schuster, 1946), p. 25.
[2] *Ibid.*, p. 14.

There are two cupfuls in a pint
Now can you tell me, Allen,
If two pints equal just one quart
Do four quarts make a _____? (gallon)

Abbreviations can be fun
And in your books are found
M-i-n. for minute stands,
And L-b. is a _____ (pound).

There are ten pennies in a dime
And in a quarter more.
In a half there are two quarters
And in a dollar _____ (four)."

The teacher smiled and told the class,
"That finishes the list;
You've answered every question right
And so it's class dis_____(missed)."[3]

COMPUTATIONS

Activities

7–33. Practice in calculating distances and time may be had by providing children with outline maps of the United States. Suggest that the locations of a dozen cities of their selection may be marked. Now each pupil may pretend that he is an important government official who is to make some political speeches. His itinerary may be planned noting flying distances and times of departure and arrival. Time zones should not be overlooked.

7–34. Some pupils may calculate minimum driving time at speed limits for a route leading from a given location in one city to a specific spot in another. First, the distance through each speed zone must be estimated. Second, calculate the driving time to the nearest minute for each zone. Third, add times and convert to hours and minutes.

---

[3] Reprinted by permission from *Exploring Arithmetic 3, Teacher's Edition* by Jesse Osborn, Adeline Riefling, and Herbert F. Spitzer. Copyright © 1962 by McGraw-Hill, Inc.

7–35. Suggest that children plan a trip by automobile to a place, or places, of interest to them. Pupils should find the gasoline mileage of the family car, kind of gasoline used and its cost, miles to be travelled, cost of fuel for the trip, etc.

7–36. Mental computation may be encouraged when children pretend they are visiting a foreign country and need to convert the centigrade temperature reports into the more familiar Fahrenheit. Usually this is done by multiplying by $\frac{9}{5}$ and then adding 32. (The Fahrenheit degree is $\frac{9}{5}$ larger than the centigrade degree.) But an approximation can be computed mentally quite readily by multiplying the centigrade reading by two, subtracting the number indicated by the tens' digit of the product, and then adding 32. For example, consider 20°C: $20 \times 2 = 40$; $40 - 4 = 36$; $36 + 32 = 68$; $20°C = 68°F$. (Note that $\frac{9}{5}$ is almost $\frac{10}{5}$ and $\frac{10}{5} = 2$. Because multiplying by two, that is, $\frac{10}{5}$, gives a product one-fifth too large, we must subtract one-fifth of the original number. Since the original number was doubled, we must compensate by subtracting half of one-fifth or one-tenth of the product, and one-tenth of a two-digit number is about that indicated by the tens' digit. We add 32 because 0°C is 32°F.)

7–37. To help children become aware of the relationship of the hypotenuse of a right triangle to the other two sides, encourage

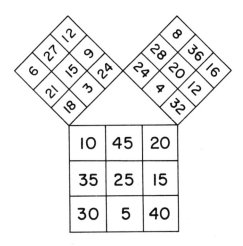

children to examine the magic squares illustrated. The square of a number in a cell of the grid (of which the hypotenuse is a side) is equal to the sum of squares of numbers in cells of the other two grids which have the same location, e.g., $10^2 = 6^2 + 8^2$. Also the square of the number which is the sum of any row, column, or diagonal of the hypotenuse grid equals the sum of numbers similarly arrived at in the other two grids. Pupils may wish to check to see if these statements are true and, perhaps, to try to make other magic squares with similar attributes.

7–38. The mathematics of musical rhythms may interest some children while providing practice in applying fractional numbers. The following musical themes use notes of various time values. Perhaps some pupils can make other themes.

7–39. Some understanding of the mathematics of navigation can be had from an activity such as the following:

A navigator on a ship near San Francisco, checking to see when the sun reached its greatest height (zenith) for the day (called "shooting the sun"), found that it did so at 8:16 Greenwich mean time. At what longitude was his ship located?

The navigator knew that time is calculated from Greenwich, England, where the longitude is 0°, and that the earth has 360° of longitude turning past the sun every 24 hours, or 1440 minutes.

By dividing 1440 by 360, he found that each degree took four minutes. 8:16 was 496 minutes of sun time from Greenwich, $496 \div 4 = 124$, so the ship was on the 124th degree of longitude west.

For pupils of high ability, give only as much data as in the first paragraph. For others give more. When this problem has been solved, give pupils various Greenwich mean times and suggest that they calculate corresponding longitudes. Or name various locations and suggest that they calculate Greenwich mean time for "high noon."

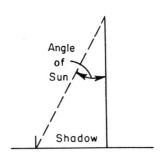

7–40. Pupils can simulate one of the earliest procedures for measuring the distance around the earth. First they should determine the angle of the sun at noon by driving a stake into the ground at a flat place, using a level to be sure that the stake is vertical. Note the end of the shadow cast by the stake; place a yardstick or other straight board from the shadow's end to the top of the stake. Measure the angle at the top. On a globe find the distance in miles from the stake to the ecliptic (where the sun is directly overhead; a good globe will have this information) at the time of year when the activity is taking place. Divide miles by degrees of the angle determined above to find how many miles correspond to one degree. Multiply by 360 to find the distance around the earth. How close did they come? Good discussion should arise from the question, why were they not exact?

7–41. The following is an activity through which fifth or sixth grade children can gain an understanding of the value of *pi*.

With rope, chalk, and measuring tape, let children work in pairs to make a half dozen circles of varying sizes on the playground. Suggest that children measure the circumference and diameter of each. When finished, the pupils may divide the number of the circumference measurement by the number of the diameter measurement. Let them compare quotients. Then average the quotients obtained to see how close to *pi* (3.1415+) they came.

Materials

See number 6–1.

Bulletin board

7–42. Encourage pupils to work at measurement problems by preparing a bulletin board carrying the title, "How Big?" Scatter on it tagboard pieces of interesting shapes each with a formula for finding its area, perimeter, radius, circumference, side, or other dimension. Provide a pocket with a ruler, pencil, and scratch pad so pupils may measure and calculate. Another pocket for depositing papers might be provided. At the end of a week check papers to see how many correct answers are found.

Game

7–43. Measurement Race. PURPOSE: to provide practice in solving measurement problems.

LEVEL: 5 to 6.

NUMBER OF PLAYERS: 2 or more.

MATERIALS NEEDED: Papers or cards with drawings of geometric figures on them. Mark measurement of length, height, radius, or other appropriate dimensions. Make some difficult by giving one measurement in inches and another in feet or yards, or show a mixture of units. Paper and pencil for players. Indicate directions, e.g., find area, perimeter, volume.

PROCEDURE: If group is large, divide pupils into small teams. At a signal the first player of each team comes to the checker (who could be the teacher) to get a card. He takes it to his desk, solves the problem, and brings his paper to the checker, then gets another card which he takes to the second player on his team. The process is repeated until each member of the team has solved a problem. Five points are given to the team completing problems first. Three points are given for each correct answer. The team with the highest score wins.

Puzzles

(Practice in solving measurement problems may be motivated through puzzles such as those below.)

7–44. Mr. McCarthy plans to fence his back yard on three sides. The plot is 50 feet across the back and 30 feet on each side. Fencing costs $40.00 per hundred feet and posts which are to be 10 feet apart cost 50¢ each. How much will his fence cost? (12 posts at 50¢ each cost $6. 110 feet of fencing at $40 per 100 feet costs $44. Total $50.)

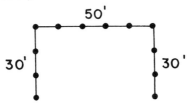

7–45. A man walks a circle road around a lake on the side of the road nearer the water. He finds that it takes him 11,450 steps. The next day he again circles the lake but this time walks on the other side of the road which is five steps wide. How many more steps will it take him? (πd = c. $\frac{22}{7}$ × d = 11,450. d = 3675 for the first walk. d is increased by 2 × 5. d = 3685. 3685 × $\frac{22}{7}$ = 11,581. 11,581 − 11,450 = about 131 steps.)

7–46. Two trains, 150 miles apart, proceed toward each other at the rate of 20 miles per hour for one and 30 miles per hour for the other. At the same time, a bird flying 75 miles per hour flies back and forth between the two trains until they crash. How far did the bird fly? (The trains move toward each other at the rate of 20 + 30 miles per hour thereby taking three hours before colliding. At 75 miles per hour for three hours, the bird flies 225 miles.)

7–47. At 3:20 P.M. a jeweler set three antique clocks to the correct time. The next afternoon at 3:20 he found that one clock was correct, one was two minutes slow, and one was two minutes fast. At those rates, how long will it take before all three clocks show 3:20 again? (Two minutes' change per day would be 60 minutes or one hour in 30 days. 30 × 12 = 360 days.)

Verses

7–48. Memory cues help some people, but for others are only amusing. Following are several verses intended to aid in the recall of the digits for π (3.1415926+). One is expected to count the letters in each word. The foreign language items are included just for fun.

English:

And I wish I could recollect
My number, known and select.
*   *   *

Now I, even I, would celebrate
In rhymes inapt, the great
Immortal Syracusan, rivall'd nevermore,
Who in his wondrous lore,
Passed on before,
Left men his guidance how to circles mensurate.
*   *   *

Sir, I send a rhyme excelling
In sacred truth and rigid spelling
Numerical sprites elucidate.

French:

Que j'aime à faire apprendre ce nombre, utile aux sages!
Immortel Archimède, sublime ingénieur, qui de ton jugement
peut sonder la valeur pour moi?
(Oh how I love to teach this number! It is so important to
the wise! Immortal Archimedes, sublime inventor (poet), who
could explain the value of your discernment for me?)

German:

Wie, o dies π macht ernstlich so vielen viele muh? Lernt
immerbin, Jünglinge, leichte verselein wie so zum Beispiel dies
mochte zu merken sein.
(Why, oh why does π give so much trouble to so many? Students,
learn easy little verses like this one!)

C O O R D I N A T E S   A N D   G R A P H S

Activities

7–49. To help children in primary grades become aware of graph principles, help them record simple data. Examples:

1. How many children in the class have dark hair (brunette)? How many light (blond)? How many medium (brown)? Discussion may show that it is necessary to arbitrarily classify a borderline case; all others are compared and listed as lighter or darker.
2. How many children have brown eyes? Blue eyes?
3. How many children's birthdays occur each month of the year?
4. How many cars of each make are in the teachers' parking lot?
5. How many children have lost teeth each month?
6. How many books has each child read this month?

Be especially alert to questions which arise naturally and which do not involve complex data.

Make a simple bar graph of data collected by cutting small (one inch is good) squares of colored paper and pasting on a chart, e.g., one square for each child with dark hair. When children have grasped the procedure, they should be encouraged to make their own graphs from data they gather. Sometimes two or three children can work together.

7–50. To give pupils practice with coordinates, arrange children's chairs in the room to form a coordinate array. Draw a diagram of it on the chalkboard. Write an ordered pair, e.g., (4,3), and suggest that the child in that location (fourth row, third chair) come to the chalkboard and write his name beside the ordered pair.

7–51. After children have learned to read graphs, some pupils (individually or in pairs) may want to make some of their own. At this point, teach or review scale drawing, e.g., $\frac{1}{2}'' = 1$ foot. Remind children that the unit relationships selected must be kept consistent for all data to be illustrated on a graph. Limit work to simple graphs such as line and bar; picture graphs, while interesting, are difficult to construct. Some examples follow.

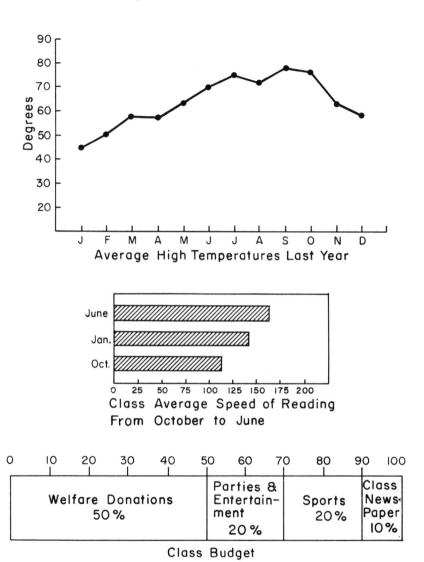

Average High Temperatures Last Year

Class Average Speed of Reading
From October to June

Class Budget

Pupils may record data and practice graphing from activities such as the following:

a. Record how many marbles are knocked out of a five foot circle by each of several players given six turns each. How many from a four foot circle? A three foot circle?

b. Record how far a simple pulley travels when the rope is pulled 12″. 24″. 36″.

c. Compare the number of words spelled correctly for each of six weeks.

d. Compare the number of hits with the number of times at bat for all members of the school or class softball team during a two-week period.

e. Drop a ball from various heights along a vertically held yardstick and record how high the bounce is. Do the same for various kinds of balls.

f. Compare the loss of water in a week's time from each of several containers with the surface area of the water in each container.

g. Record the weekly growth of plants "watered" with tap water, coke, rubbing alcohol, water mixed with liquid fertilizer, or the like. Do the same using tap water but of different amounts for each plant.

h. Compare heights of boys or girls in the class with their weights.

Bulletin board

7–52. To help children recognize the usefulness of graphs make a bulletin board on which are examples of graphs cut from magazines and/or newspapers. Frame questions which can be answered by referring to posted items. Provide scratch pad and pencil.

Games

7–53. Find the Point. PURPOSE: to provide pupils with practice in locating the coordinates of points.

LEVEL: 3 to 6.

NUMBER OF PLAYERS: 2 or more.

MATERIALS NEEDED: Graph paper for each player, and a spinner as in "Out of the Red" (number 2–42).

PROCEDURE: Distribute graph paper and direct players to draw a coordinate plane marking both X and Y axis from negative nine to positive nine. Divide group into teams. Leader spins twice and records ordered pair, e.g., ($^-3$, $^+4$). Players locate point and mark it. Repeat four times. Instruct players to join the four points using a ruler and making heavy pencil marks. All hold up paper so leader can check. The shape of the figure will indicate who has made errors. Give each team as many points as there are correct figures.

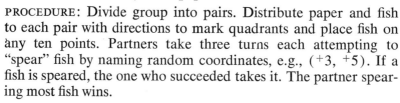

7–54. Spearfishing. PURPOSE: to provide practice in naming coordinates.

LEVEL: 5 to 6.

NUMBER OF PLAYERS: 2 or more.

MATERIALS: For every two players, graph paper with large squares (½ inch) and ten very small paper "fish."

PROCEDURE: Divide group into pairs. Distribute paper and fish to each pair with directions to mark quadrants and place fish on any ten points. Partners take three turns each attempting to "spear" fish by naming random coordinates, e.g., ($^+3$, $^+5$). If a fish is speared, the one who succeeded takes it. The partner spearing most fish wins.

7–55. Thirty-six and Out. PURPOSE: to provide practice in finding points in a quadrant.

LEVEL: 5 to 6.

NUMBER OF PLAYERS: 2.

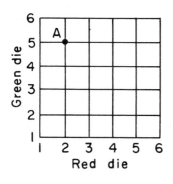

MATERIALS NEEDED: Two dice of different color and two sheets of paper with 6 x 6 grids (see diagram).

PROCEDURE: Play alternates between the two players. Each player shakes and rolls the dice and then circles the point on his graph corresponding to the combination shown on the dice. For example, if the first player rolls red 2 and green 5 then he will circle point A, whose coordinates are (2, 5), as shown. The second player then rolls the dice and circles a point on his board.

If a player rolls a double (same number on each die), he gets another turn. If a combination rolled is a duplication of a previous play, no point is circled.

The first player to circle all 36 points is the winner.

Chapter 8

WORD PROBLEMS

Materials

8–1. To provide practice in problem solving, write story problems on the outside of envelopes. Inside, place 3″ x 5″ cards on which there are steps leading to a solution and the answer. After pupils have worked problems, they may check the cards for correctness.

8–2. To vary problem solving practice, invite pupils to write original problems on one side of a large card (6″ x 8″ is good) with the steps leading to the solution shown on the reverse side. File according to approximate difficulty or processes employed for solution (or both). Problem cards may be assigned or simply made available to pupils who need practice.

8–3. To provide practice in applying arithmetic to purchasing situations, gather a supply of mail order catalogs. Duplicate order blanks. Distribute, or let children select, assignment cards on which are items such as, "Prepare an order for supplies needed to make a small vegetable garden in a back yard. Don't forget to include postage and tax." "If you have $20.00 to spend for presents for members of your family, what would you order?

Fill out all necessary parts of the order blank." Or, "Pretend that you have been told you may order up to $30.00 of anything that interests you. Fill out an order form being sure that the total does not exceed $30.00 even with tax and postage."

8–4. For additional practice in applied arithmetic, mount advertisements from newspapers on cardboard. These may be for stores selling groceries, hardware, sporting goods, varieties, radios, etc. Make up problems from some of the data found in the ads, e.g., "How much would you have to pay for two dozen eggs, three quarts of milk, and one box of crackers?" Simple but realistic problems may be solved mentally and only the answers recorded. Vary the difficulty according to the needs of individuals. Advanced pupils may calculate tax, discounts, or time payments where appropriate.

Two other materials useful in teaching word problems are found in numbers 3–25 and 3–26.

Bulletin Boards

8–5. To encourage practical application of arithmetic, display a large newspaper grocery store advertisement. On strips of paper, write questions such as, "What is the cost of three dozen Grade A eggs?" Provide a pad of paper and a pencil for pupils' responses.

8–6. Do the same as above, but use other types of advertisements. Do not overlook hardware, paint, sporting goods, auto supplies, and other male interests.

Games

8–7. I've Got It! PURPOSE: to provide practice in problem solving.

LEVEL: 2 to 6.

NUMBER OF PLAYERS: 2 or more (adaptable to individual play).

MATERIALS NEEDED: Small cards on which problems are typed; large cards containing answers to problems (two or more cards answer each problem).

PROCEDURE: Distribute five or more answer cards to each player. Teacher, or leader, reads a problem from a small card. Pupils who have answers raise their hands. The first to do so may give the answer. If he is correct, he may have the problem card; if he is wrong, the second pupil to raise his hand may give his answer. The player accumulating the most problem cards is the winner.

"I've Got It!" can be adapted for individual play by writing answers on small cards. A player is to match answers with problems. Store in a stocking box or large manila envelope.

8–8. Mathematical Baseball. PURPOSE: to provide practice in problem solving.

LEVEL: 2 to 6.

NUMBER OF PLAYERS: 4 to 20.

MATERIALS NEEDED: Cards on which problems for mental arithmetic are written. Mark them "single," "double," "triple," or "home run," according to difficulty. Four places in the room designated as first, second, third, and home bases.

PROCEDURE: Divide group into two teams. One player on each team is selected to be pitcher. The team members "at bat" line up at front of room. The opposing pitcher reads a problem and the first player gives his answer. If correct he takes whatever base the problem calls for. If he is wrong, an "out" is called. Three outs and the side is retired. If the first player gets a single, he may score a run if another player gets a triple before the side has three outs. As in baseball, only runs count for scores.

8–9. Problem Race. PURPOSE: to provide practice in problem solving.

LEVEL: 2 to 6.

NUMBER OF PLAYERS: 2 or more.

MATERIALS NEEDED: A set of problem papers which will take the average pupil about one half hour to complete (less for grades two and three).

PROCEDURE: If the group is small, play as individuals; divide larger groups into two or more teams. Distribute papers face down to each player. At a signal, all turn up papers and begin. As each finishes, he raises his pencil. The first to complete gets a score of 20, the next 19, and so on. When about two-thirds of the players have finished, call "time" and all lay pencils on desks. Those not done get the next score whatever it may be. Check papers and add three points to each player's score for every correctly solved problem. The individual or team with the highest score wins.

8–10. Man on the Moon. PURPOSE: to provide practice in problem solving.

LEVEL: 2 to 6.

NUMBER OF PLAYERS: 2 or more.

MATERIALS NEEDED: Chart or chalkboard drawing of Earth and Moon. Mark spaces between Earth and Moon according to number of players. To mark these as distances divide 237,000 miles (the distance between the two bodies) by the number of players.

PROCEDURE: On a series of cards write computations or word problems on which pupils need practice; number each card and record number and answer on a checker's sheet. Divide group into teams. Distribute cards face down to players. At a signal the first two turn up cards and work problems. When finished, check against answer sheet. If correct, each team's rocket ship moves one space toward Moon. Proceed similarly with other pairs of players until all have had turns. See if either ship reaches Moon or is "lost in space."

If the group is large, divide into several teams to reduce waiting time for those not actively solving problems.

8–11. Arithmetic Race. PURPOSE: to provide practice in problem solving.

LEVEL: 3 to 6.

NUMBER OF PLAYERS: 4 or more.

MATERIALS NEEDED: Computation or problem-solving sheets of paper for each team; items should be either identical or similar in difficulty. There should be as many problems as there are players on each team.

PROCEDURE: Divide players into as many relay teams as desired; arrange pupils in rows or designate order if children are at tables. Distribute papers face down, one to the first player of each team. At a signal each works the first problem and then passes the paper on to the second player who must check the work of the first one; if the second player is satisfied that it is correct, he then works the second one. The third player checks the work of the one preceding him and then works the third problem, and so on. The last player returns the sheet to the first player for checking. The team first completing all problems correctly is the winner.

8–12. Around the World. PURPOSE: to provide practice in problem solving.

LEVEL: 3 to 6.

NUMBER OF PLAYERS: 2 or more.

MATERIALS NEEDED: A set of papers containing five problems. A large circle on the chalkboard showing the home town and four stops for a flight "around the world."

PROCEDURE: Distribute papers with instructions to work problems. Each problem correctly solved is a "ticket" for part of the flight around the world. The object is to see how many persons can get all the way around the world; some may be stuck in Calcutta or elsewhere.

8–13. Off to Pluto. PURPOSE: to provide practice in problem solving.

LEVEL: 3 to 6.

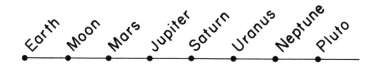

NUMBER OF PLAYERS: 2 to 8.

MATERIALS NEEDED: A line segment drawn on the chalkboard to indicate progression from Earth to Pluto. Paper "space ships" for each player with masking tape on the back so they can be moved from place to place along the "space path." A set of seven problems for each player.

PROCEDURE: Line up "space ships" at Earth position. Distribute papers face down. At a signal, all players begin solving problems. As each finishes a problem, he raises his hand; the teacher or leader comes to his desk and checks his work. If correct, his space ship is moved to Moon position. When a second problem is correctly solved, the space ship is moved to Mars position. The object is to see who can reach Pluto first.

If pressure for speed is too great for pupils, make the object to get to Pluto without trying to be first to do so.

8–14. Eraser Relay. PURPOSE: to provide practice in problem solving.

LEVEL: 3 to 6.

NUMBER OF PLAYERS: 2 or more.

MATERIALS NEEDED: Chalk erasers and chalkboards; cards marked with arithmetic examples or problems.

PROCEDURE: Divide players into two or more teams depending on the size of the group. Shuffle cards and divide them into as many stacks as there are teams; place face down at the end of the room opposite the chalkboard. At a signal, the first player of each team places an eraser on his head and goes to a given stack of cards, draws the top one, and proceeds to the chalkboard where he must do the example or problem; he then writes the answer in a designated place, erases his work, lays his card in the chalktray, and gives his eraser to the next player on his team. If a player's eraser falls from his head, he must pick it up and replace it before proceeding. Play continues until all have had a turn. Answers are checked and the team which has most correct answers is the winner; in case of a tie, the team finishing first wins.

8–15. Grand Champion. PURPOSE: to provide practice in problem solving.

LEVEL: 3 to 6.

NUMBER OF PLAYERS: 2 or more.

MATERIALS NEEDED: A set of cards, each with a computation example or a story problem on which practice is needed; at least three cards for each player. Number each card and prepare an answer sheet. Paper and pencil for each person. Bag.

PROCEDURE: Place cards in bag. Each player reaches into bag and draws three cards which he places face down before him. At a signal all players turn up cards and work examples or problems on their paper. As each finishes, he holds up his pencil. Leader records names in order of completion. When most of the players have finished, check the answers of those first to finish. The first who has all correct is declared Grand Champion. If the group is large, the next three to finish correctly may be declared runners-up.

8–16. Hard-boiled Egg. PURPOSE: to provide practice in problem solving.

LEVEL: 3 to 6.

NUMBER OF PLAYERS: 2 or more.

MATERIALS NEEDED: Duplicated papers containing examples or story problems on which practice is needed. A kitchen timer.

PROCEDURE: Distribute papers face down before each player. Set timer for ten minutes or as appropriate to the ability of the pupils and the difficulty of the material. Give signal to begin with instructions to stop when the timer bell sounds. The one who gets most done correctly is given the title of Hard-boiled Egg. Other players may then complete their papers and all whose work is correct are dubbed Soft-boiled Eggs.

8–17. World Series. PURPOSE: to provide practice in problem solving.

LEVEL: 3 to 6.

NUMBER OF PLAYERS: 2 or more.

MATERIALS NEEDED: Four half-sheets of paper for each player. Chalk and chalkboard.

PROCEDURE: Distribute four half-sheets of paper to each player. Divide group into two teams and name them for baseball teams. After giving instructions to write names on paper, write a problem on the chalkboard and have children proceed solving at once. As each contestant completes his work, he brings his paper to the teacher's desk and places it face down at a designated place. When all have finished, ask one person to work the problem on the chalkboard. If all agree that it is correct, turn pile of papers right side up and give 50 points to first correct paper, 49 to next, then 48, and so on. Zero for incorrect papers. Captains record scores on chalkboard as they are given and compute scores for their teams. Repeat the process four to seven times for a "World Series." The team with four wins is declared "World Champion."

8–18. Double or Nothing. PURPOSE: to provide practice in mental arithmetic.

LEVEL: 3 to 6.

NUMBER OF PLAYERS: 2 or more.

MATERIALS NEEDED: A set of cards on back of which is a problem that can be solved mentally. The items are graduated in difficulty.

PROCEDURE: Small groups play as teams of two or three. An "MC" is selected and given the set of problems arranged from easy to difficult. The first player or team comes up to the MC who says, "You have ten points. How much of it will you risk?" When the contestant(s) has decided, he is given a problem. If two or more pupils are working as a team, they may confer with each other before deciding on an answer. If correct, the amount risked is doubled and added to the unrisked score, e.g., if five points were risked, a correct answer would give $(2 \times 5) + 5$ or 15 points. If the answer is not correct, the contestant(s) loses the amount risked. Two consecutive misses retire the player(s). Highest score wins.

8–19. Information Please. PURPOSE: to provide practice in mental arithmetic.

LEVEL: 3 to 6.

NUMBER OF PLAYERS: 3 or more.

MATERIALS NEEDED: A toy table microphone for the teacher's desk and a floor "mike" for the front of the room. A set of problems which can be solved mentally or a set of questions asking how certain types of problems are solved, e.g., How does one find the area of a triangle?

PROCEDURE: Select a master of ceremonies who sits at the desk with a mike and a set of problems. If the group is small, all players line up so that each player can step quickly to the floor mike to give his answer to the problem given him by the MC. For larger groups send sets of five or six players at a time to the mike area. While groups are changing places, the MC may give station identification and perhaps an advertisement for a local business.

8–20. Problem Master. PURPOSE: to provide practice in matching equations with problems.

LEVEL: 4 to 6.

NUMBER OF PLAYERS: 2 or more.

MATERIALS NEEDED: Chalk and chalkboard. Clock with second hand or egg timer.

PROCEDURE: One child is selected to be Problem Master. He writes an equation with one variable on the chalkboard and selects another player to make up a problem to fit the equation. If he can do so and give the answer within the time limit (vary according to group—try one minute to begin with) he becomes Problem Master; otherwise the first one continues. The one who can be Problem Master for the largest number of problems is winner.

8–21. Overland Championship. PURPOSE: to provide practice in solving problems by using an equivalent ratio procedure.

LEVEL: 6.

NUMBER OF PLAYERS: 2 or more.

MATERIALS NEEDED: Duplicated road chart similar to illustration. A set of problems to be solved by an equivalent ratio procedure; e.g., If your car goes 22 miles per gallon of gasoline, how many gallons are needed to drive from Oak Point to Tippy? Solution:

$$\text{Distance} \quad \begin{array}{r} 44 \\ 19 \\ +28 \\ \hline 91 \text{ miles} \end{array} \qquad \frac{1}{22} = \frac{n}{91} \quad 22n = 91 \quad n = 4\,\tfrac{3}{22} \text{ gals.}$$

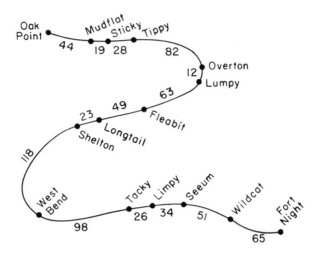

If your car travels from Longtail to West Bend on 5⅞ gallons of gasoline, how many miles per gallon are you getting? Solution:

Distance 23 $\dfrac{1}{n} = \dfrac{5⅞}{141}$ 5⅞ n = 141   n = 24 miles/gal.
        +118
       141 miles

Colored paper cutouts of cars marked first, second, third, fourth for winners' prizes.

PROCEDURE: Distribute road charts among players. Let each player select his own variety of stock car for the championship race. Explain that to win in this road race, the drivers must correctly complete a set of problems. The order of finishing will be recorded. When most have "crossed the finish line," the papers will be checked and the first four with correct papers will be given prizes; those who make mistakes will be disqualified. Either write the problems on the chalkboard or distribute papers, face down, on which problems appear. At the gun (clap of hands) the race begins. Winners come forward for awards ceremony.

VARIATION: Write answers to problems in each road section in random order. Provide players with beans or other markers to place on the appropriate road chart section as each problem is solved. See who can first fill all the sections.

For other games which can be adapted to practice with word problems, see numbers 3–108, 3–109, and 6–22.

Puzzles

See numbers 5–43, 6–29, 7–44, 7–45, 7–46.

GLOSSARY WITH REFERENCES

Here are explanations of terms used in the text which are not common to the "old arithmetic" (Terms explained in the text are not included). Boldface references are to item numbers in which the term is first used, chapters 2–8, inclusive.

ABACUS. A mechanical device used for computations. It usually has large beads on wires or rods, each of which denotes a place value. **2–9.**

ACUTE ANGLE TRIANGLE. A triangle all angles of which measure less than a right angle. **5–28.**

ALGORISM. A pattern for performing an arithmetic computation. The algorism for $3 \times 27 = 81$ is 27.

$$\frac{\times 3}{81}$$

2–103.

ASSOCIATIVE. A property (sometimes called a law or a principle) of addition or multiplication such that the sum or product is not affected by the way in which the numbers are grouped, as $(2 + 3) + 4 = 9$ and $2 + (3 + 4) = 9$. **2–106.**

CHORD. A line segment having its endpoints on a circle. A diameter may be thought of as the longest chord. **5–27.**

CLOSURE. A property of a given operation on members of a set the answer to which is in the set, e.g., the sum of any two natural numbers is a natural number. The set of natural numbers is said to be closed under addition. **2–106.**

COMMUTATIVE. A property (sometimes called a law or a principle) of addition or multiplication such that the sum or product of two numbers is not affected by the order in which the numbers are added or multiplied, as $4 + 3 = 3 + 4$. **2–106.**

COMPOSITE NUMBER. An integer greater than one having more than two factors. (See prime number.) **2–13.**

COORDINATE. One of a set of numbers locating a point in space. If the point is known to be on a given line, one coordinate is needed; if on a plane, two are needed; if in space, three are needed. **7–50.**

CUISENAIRE RODS. A set of colored rods designed by George Cuisenaire, a Belgian educator, in which pieces range in length from one to ten centimeters. All pieces of a given length are of the same color. The set of rods is used in teaching various mathematics concepts. **2–8.**

DIGIT. Any of the ten figures, 0, 1, 2, 3, 4, 5, 6, 7, 8, 9, commonly used as one of the symbols in a place value numeral. **2–29.**

DIRECTED NUMBERS. Another term for the set of integers. **2–46.**

DISJOINT SETS. Sets are said to be disjoint if they have no elements in common. **2–95.**

DISTRIBUTIVE. A property (sometimes called a law or a principle) which in elementary school arithmetic is usually applied to the multiplication of two numbers one of which is an indicated sum, as $2 \times (4 + 3)$. The multiplication is said to be "distributive in respect to addition." Example: $2 \times (4 + 3) = (2 \times 4) + (2 \times 3)$. Under certain circumstances, the distributive property may apply also to multiplication over subtraction and to division over addition or subtraction. **2–106.**

EQUILATERAL TRIANGLE. A triangle having three equal sides. **5–10.**

EXPANDED NOTATION. A numeral written so as to show the place value of each digit, as $187 = 100 + 80 + 7$ or $(1 \times 10^2) + (8 \times 10^1) + (7 \times 10^0)$. **2–88.**

FACTOR. One of two or more numbers to be multiplied to form a product; e.g., 2 and 7 are factors of 14, since $2 \times 7 = 14$. **2–103.**

HEXAGON. A polygon having six sides. **5–28.**

IDENTITY ELEMENT. A number which does not change the value of another number when a given operation is performed. Zero is the identity element under addition, e.g., $5 + 0 = 5$. One is the identity element under multiplication, e.g., $5 \times 1 = 5$. **2–106.**

INTEGER. The set of numbers generated by beginning with zero and adding and subtracting ones— . . . $^-2$, $^-1$, 0, $^+1$, $^+2$, . . . **2–41.**

INTERSECTION. In geometry, the point or points common to two or more geometric lines or figures. In set theory, a subset consisting of members common to two or more sets. **2–106.**

LINE SEGMENT. A part of a line with two endpoints. **5–26.**

NOTATION. Symbols used to express quantities, operations, or relations. Examples: 6, +, =. **2–74.**

NUMBER. A concept of quantity. The symbol for a number is called a numeral. **2–1.**

NUMBER LINE. A drawing to represent a line on which points are associated with numbers. **2–44.**

NUMBER SYSTEM. A set of numbers on which one may perform operations (such as addition or multiplication) and to which certain properties apply. Elementary school children work with natural numbers (1, 2, 3, 4, . . .), whole numbers (0, 1, 2, 3, . . .), integers (. . . ⁻2, ⁻1, 0, ⁺1, ⁺2, . . .), rational numbers (the integers and fractional numbers, both positive and negative), and, in a very limited way, real numbers (rational and irrational numbers). **2–3.**

NUMERAL. A symbol for a number. A given number may have many symbols, e.g., 9, 3 × 3, 10 − 1, IX, etc. **2–1.**

NUMERATION SYSTEM. A system used to represent numbers. The Hindu-Arabic numeration system consists of the symbols (called digits) 0, 1, 2, 3, 4, 5, 6, 7, 8, 9; digits are combined to form numerals for numbers greater than 9, e.g., 47 (the 4 as here used represents 4 tens; hence 47 = 40 + 7). See 2–68 to 2–73. Certain principles govern each numeration system; for the Hindu-Arabic system the principles are (1) the use of zero, (2) a base of ten, (3) place value, and (4) addition (as 186 = 100 + 80 + 6). **2–4.**

OBTUSE ANGLE TRIANGLE. A triangle having an interior angle measuring more than 90°. **5–28.**

OCTAGON. A polygon having eight sides. **5–28.**

ORDERED PAIR. Usually refers to two numbers given in a special order and written as (2, 4). The order may be important, as in finding a point on a graph. **3–9.**

PENTAGON. A polygon having five sides. **5–28.**

PLACE VALUE. A property of a numeration system which gives digits different values according to their positions, e.g., in 409 of the Hindu-Arabic numeration system, the 9 is in the ones' place, the 0 in the tens' place, and the 4 in the hundreds' place. **2–4.**

POLYGON. A plane, closed geometric figure consisting of three or more line segments. **5–19.**

POLYHEDRON. A solid figure bounded by plane polygons. **5–17.**

PRIME NUMBER. An integer greater than one having only two factors, itself and one. The first five prime numbers in the natural number system are 2, 3, 5, 7, and 11. **2–12.**

PROPERTY. A characteristic of a mathematical object, such as that place value is a property of the Hindu-Arabic numeration system, or that the commutative law is a property of the addition of whole numbers. **2–110.**

QUADRILATERAL. A polygon having four sides. **5–28.**

RATIO. The comparison of two quantities. If a school class has 12 boys and 17 girls, the ratio of boys to girls is 12 to 17—usually written as $\frac{12}{17}$ or as 12:17.   **2–103.**

RECIPROCAL. Two numbers are said to be reciprocals if their product is 1. $\frac{4}{3}$ is the reciprocal of $\frac{3}{4}$ since $\frac{4}{3} \times \frac{3}{4} = 1$.   **2–110.**

RELATION SIGN. A symbol used to indicate a comparison of two objects. If numbers are compared, three symbols are common: = (equal to), > (greater than), and < (less than).   **2–2.**

RHOMBUS. A parallelogram with two adjacent sides equal (hence all four sides are equal).   **5–28.**

SCALENE TRIANGLE. A triangle with no two sides equal.   **5–28.**

SET. A collection of particular things, as the set of marbles in Tony's pocket, the set of numbers between 10 and 20, or the set of points on a line segment. Some synonyms are herd, bunch, flock, bundle, pride, carload, pile.   **2–4.**

SIMPLE CLOSED CURVE. This may be represented by a figure so drawn that it ends where it began and the path followed does not cross or retrace itself, as circles, squares, ovals.   **5–26.**

SUBSET. A set such that all of its members are also members of another set, e.g., the set of boys in this class is a subset of the set of children in this class.   **2–7.**

TOPOLOGY. A branch of geometry concerned with those properties of figures which remain unchanged even if the figures are deformed. The sides of a square can be transformed so as to form a circle; the points and planes are unchanged. Topology is sometimes referred to as "rubber sheet geometry."   **5–29.**

TRAPEZOID. A quadrilateral having one pair of parallel, but not equal, sides.   **5–28.**

TRICHOTOMY OF RELATIONS. The three most common relations between a pair of numbers: more than (>), equal to (=), and less than (<).   **2–2.**

VENN DIAGRAM. A drawing used to show the operations on or the relations among (or between) sets.   **2–95.**

LIST OF GAMES

*Numbers following game titles refer to Chapter and item number.

INDEX

For major topics, see Contents, page iii, or the content listing at beginning of each chapter.